CW00746943

THE GOODWOOD PHANTOM

THE GOODWOOD PHANTOM

Dawn of a New Era

MALCOLM TUCKER

The Goodwood Phantom
Dawn of a New Era

by Malcolm Tucker

First published 2004

ISBN Casebound: 1-85443-210-9
ISBN Special Edition: 1-85443-211-7

Printed in England by

The Lavenham Press
47 Water Street, Lavenham,
Suffolk CO10 9RN,
England

for the publisher

Dalton Watson Fine Books
1 Arundel Court, Elverlands Close,
Ferring, West Sussex BN12 5QE,
England

1730 Christopher Drive,
Deerfield, IL 60015,
USA

www.daltonwatson.com

ACKNOWLEDGEMENTS AND DEDICATION

To be the writer of a book such as this, part historical record, part technical detail and part interpretation of facts, places one in the position of being the captain of a team. It is to the following 'team members', who have so kindly given of their time and effort to enable me to record the events and endeavours leading to the creation of the Rolls-Royce Phantom motor car, that I express my sincere thanks:

Rolls-Royce Motor Cars Ltd. employees, past and present: Karl-Heinz Kalbfell, former director of Project Rolls-Royce and since May 2004 chairman and chief executive of Rolls-Royce Motor Cars Ltd.; Tony Gott, former chairman and chief executive; Ian Cameron, chief designer; Marek Djordjevic, exterior designer; Charles Coldham, interior designer; Dieter Udelhoven, former director, manufacturing; Karl Baumer, former director, engineering; Dr. Tim Leverton, former chief engineer; Carsten Pries, former general manager, strategy and control; Fred Fruth, general manager, public affairs; Graham Biggs, head of corporate communications; Howard Mosher, director, sales and marketing; and Jonathan Stanley, product public relations manager.

A special thanks to marketing director Axel Oesterling and Rolls-Royce product manager Stefan Conrady, whose support made the venture possible, and to dealer marketing manager Tina Lawaczeck, who arranged interviews, manufacturing plant tours and numerous archive retrievals. The members of the workforce at Goodwood who allowed me to disrupt their working days must be congratulated for their patience.

At Goodwood, I have been greatly helped by Lord March, Zanny Gilchrist and Rob Widdows.

Finally, my thanks to the team behind Dalton Watson itself: to my publisher Glyn Morris, my editor Giles Chapman, and to Mike Lawrence and Martin Buckley for their invaluable written contributions. On the visual and presentation side, the designer, Simon Loxley, and Christine Lalla, whose intriguing black-and-white photographic studies of the Phantom have added greatly to the book.

This book is dedicated to the memory of Sir Henry Royce; the designers, engineers and all the employees past and present who have produced Rolls-Royce motor cars; and to my father, Arthur Tucker, who introduced me to the pleasures of Rolls-Royce motoring.

CONTENTS

INTRODUCTION

Along with many boys growing up in the late 1950s and early 1960s, I had a liking for sports cars of all kinds. Unusually for someone of my age, however, my passion was for those wonderful beasts built in the 1920s and 1930s. Living in west London, I often encountered tired out, battle-scarred quality cars from that seemingly golden age; they languished, on bald tyres, in droves on the side streets of Notting Hill and Shepherd's Bush. One apparently abandoned member of their ranks was a Rolls-Royce 20hp. It rested by a steeply cambered kerbside, its deflating tyres adding to the Tower of Pisa-like lean of its forlorn, sporting coachwork. Windows were cracked, the radiator was almost green with verdigris and the bodywork was crumpled, patched and matt grey. Somehow, though, this car had an attraction and grandeur all its own – true quality just visible beneath its smog-stained countenance. I was completely smitten.

People say good luck comes in batches of three: my burgeoning interest in Rolls-Royce certainly seemed to support this theory because next in my triumvirate came a pair of Phantom II limousines. My father had bought a Vauxhall dealership and with it came a car hire business. The Phantoms were backed up by a fleet of more modern (albeit more plebeian) Austin Princesses, the former to be kept by the previous owner of the dealership, so I rode in one of these ancient, august Rolls-Royce motor cars only once. It was that ride which introduced me to the special qualities that had made Rolls-Royces 'The Best Car in the World'. I was intrigued by the power of the car and how quietly it was delivered. Its smoothness, the way everything seemed pleasant to touch or use, began to fascinate me – I had to find out more. The delight in sports cars was a thing of the past. There were now only two kinds of cars for me: those built by Rolls-Royce, and all the rest.

My third draught from the Rolls-Royce tankard was a 1957 Silver Cloud, which became our family car in 1962. My father kept it for the next 25 years and I learnt to drive in it, a fact noted by *The Autocar*'s correspondent 'Scribe' when he heard about my unusually exotic introduction to motoring. I joined the Rolls-Royce Enthusiasts' Club while still a schoolboy and acquired my first 'proper' car in 1968, a 1952 Bentley Mk.VI. Since then I have owned at least 20 more Rolls-Royce built cars, plus I have served as chairman of the Rolls-Royce Enthusiasts' Club. In all these years, my interest in the cars has only grown, so when news broke of Rolls-Royce Motor Cars' radical release from its unbroken British custodianship, I was concerned.

I was aware there was no longer a British company with sufficient engineering experience, nor the sheer funds, to foster a future for Rolls-Royce Motor Cars. Like many enthusiasts, I knew the company needed

Inspiration for the design studio workers in the form of the Spirit of Ecstasy, made from clay trimmings from a styling scale model of the Phantom.

a purchaser with a highly developed technological capacity, a strong desire to allow Rolls-Royce to retain its precious essence, and the self-control and vision to prevent it becoming just another hollow, upmarket 'brand' name. Deep pockets, no doubt, would also be required, for the purchase of a car company is but the down payment for developing the new models that lie ahead.

All these factors meant a German buyer, either BMW, Daimler-Benz or Volkswagen, was almost inevitable. Arguably with the possible exception of Toyota, they are the best-managed, most innovative and most quality-driven carmakers on the planet. All three had the right credentials but, when the 'For Sale' sign became detectable through the swirling smokescreen surrounding Rolls-Royce as the 20th century drew to a close, which was it to be? And most importantly, what sort of new Rolls-Royce cars would be created?

It is a mystery no longer. BMW has taken over the guardianship of Rolls-Royce Motor Cars Ltd. To the delight of enthusiasts, BMW states 'Rolls-Royce is something special' and the magnificent new Phantom is the embodiment of this. So the reader can imagine what a pleasure it has been for me to research and write the definitive story of the Phantom, its outstanding genesis, and its amazing new home in the Sussex countryside. Even more so because it is for Dalton Watson, a publishing name inextricably linked to Rolls-Royce for the last 40 years. That has been my endeavour in this book. Whether you own a Phantom, have one on order, or simply admire the vision behind the creation of great motor cars, I trust *The Goodwood Phantom* proves to be truly illuminating.

Malcolm Tucker
Hampshire, UK, 2004

Part 1

HOW PROJECT ROLLS-ROYCE WAS BORN

1 DRIVING THE PHANTOM

There is no evidence of an engine power until that power is required. Then it comes in a volume and with a fluency that is almost incredible, having regard to the absence of any sign of sensible effort in its delivery

– ROLLS-ROYCE PHANTOM II SALES BROCHURE, 1929

Opposite: an autumn day driving through the Sussex countryside – the perfect way to enjoy the Phantom.

There is no doubt about it; the new, Goodwood-built Phantom is a very large car indeed. It has presence. It has style. It deserves precedence. But, in classic owner/driver fashion, the car also invites the onlooker to get behind the wheel.

Approach the car and walk around it. A lot of the massive frontal appearance apparent in some pictures is just not there in reality, and the subtlety of the sweep and flow of the body becomes more evident the longer it is studied. There are hints of earlier Rolls-Royce models: from one angle you see some Silver Shadow, from another, so much Silver Cloud, and elsewhere an undeniable link to the coachbuilt limousines of the 1950s. Less obvious, almost subliminal, are such dimensions as the ratio between wheel size and body height, the rise of the door sills and the shape of the window glass.

This is not a retrospective recreation: the Phantom is an up-to-the-minute interpretation of the traditional, formal British coachbuilt saloon. Many a pint of best British bitter will be consumed as Rolls-Royce enthusiasts discuss the pros and cons of the frontal aspect of the car. The radiator shell is truly vast and the rectangular headlights do look strange on first acquaintance, but given the design brief for the Phantom, it all makes sense.

The door handles look modern, and give no visual clue as to how they might operate, but grasp one and it is obvious it should be gently pulled. As with many a pre-war car, these door handles are pleasurable to use and give the first hint that one is about to experience a machine designed to demonstrate precision engineering, uncompromisingly built on a human scale – for human enjoyment.

Once inside, the driver will quickly become familiar with the environment and controls. This will be the first experience of the 'Authority Concept' that has been at the core of the design brief for the Phantom. Rolls-Royce Motor Cars created a new vocabulary to describe this car, the 'Authority Concept' being a prime example. It starts with the driving position itself. Once adjusted, the seat will allow a commanding view of the road ahead, the driver's eye line being about midway between that in a luxury saloon and a Range Rover. The bonnet with its characteristic chrome divider, recalling the central double-hinge from Silver Cloud days, is in full view. The slightly domed edges of the wings offer a gentle recollection of the Silver Shadow. And, of course, the Spirit of Ecstasy radiator mascot leads the way.

The steering wheel is absolutely central to the driver's seat, and so are the pedals. Hands naturally grasp the large-diameter, thin-rimmed wheel at the 'twenty-to-four' position, giving relaxed and comfortable control. The horn is sounded by pressing either of the

GWD 968

The typically thin-rimmed Rolls-Royce steering wheel enhances driver confidence when cornering fast.

two upper wheel spokes, and the hi-fi, mobile telephone and satellite navigation system can be operated by convex and concave chromium buttons on the centre hub. In so many ways, one only has to reach out for the naturally anticipated position of a control, and there it is. Rolls-Royce calls this part of its 'Authority Concept' the 'Intuitive Control'. Balance, proportion, precision, alignment, ease of control and harmony are other elements, all of which endow the Phantom with the uncanny ability to keep on course, despite the distance the car puts between a driver and the world outside.

Rolls-Royce has recognised that available technology and the resulting complexity of modern cars can easily lead designers to include a plethora of confusing secondary controls. At the same time, higher road speeds and denser traffic make the manipulation of these knobs, buttons, levers and touch-sensitive screens increasingly dangerous. In the Phantom, primary controls are intuitive. Want to select a radio station? Push the large, gleaming chrome knob directly below the radio and turn for volume. Choose one of the six preset stations by pressing a 'violin tuning key'-styled switch, three flanking each side of the frequency display. All other audio controls are in the same area but of a different configuration so the driver's eyes do not need to leave the road ahead – the sense of touch is enough.

Similarly, the air-conditioning controls are grouped neatly below the main facia. Temperature is controlled by a wheel-type dial rotating through a vertical axis and

Above: wheel-mounted controls, column-mounted gear selector and facia switchbox are all in best Rolls-Royce tradition.

Right: the 'Controller' released from its centre armrest housing cubby.

Far right: satin sterling for surrounds and polished sterling finishes for manual controls.

Seat, steering wheel and pedals in perfect alignment; on the dashboard, the analogue clock panel rolls back to reveal the Controller information screen. Below that is the radio, the climate control selectors and the air-conditioning controls.

fan speed by knobs rotating on a longitudinal axis. All so simple. The traditional 'eyeball' air vents with their organ stop controls have the added refinement, when moved, of actuating motors to slowly open the vents – avoiding an unseemly rush of air into the car's interior.

So what of the secondary controls which are conspicuous by their absence? They come under the heading of 'Functionality upon request'. Some, like the electric seat positioners, are hidden in compartments such as the centre armrests, and many are operated by the 'Controller'. Similar in concept to the BMW iDrive system, the Controller is a solid metal knob normally hidden from view in the front central armrest. Open the armrest compartment and the dash-mounted clock panel rotates to reveal a 6.5 inch monitor. The display can be altered by turning and pushing the Controller in any of four directions: forward, back and to left and right. The menu options displayed on the screen mimic the movements of the Controller, reinforcing once again the intuitive concept of the Phantom's design. For the sake of clarity, the eight main menus offered on the BMW iDrive system have been condensed to four for contemporary Rolls-Royce drivers: Communication, Navigation, Entertainment and Configuration (for vehicle settings), with no loss of finesse. Interestingly, having been pioneered on the Phantom, this logical simplification of the original BMW 7 Series iDrive has now been adopted for the new 5 Series.

Rolls-Royce has retained the traditional switchbox for ignition key, starter button and lights, although it has been designed utilising today's technology. Likewise the gear selector, mounted on the right of the steering column with a central 'enunciator panel' visible through the steering wheel, is immediately familiar to drivers of every previous model back to the Silver Shadow.

Once the car is fired up, a little engine vibration can be sensed until the correct operating temperature is reached; thereafter the driver would need to check the instruments to be absolutely sure the engine is actually running, so smooth is the delivery of power at idle. Directly ahead of the driver, a little lower than might be expected, is a central speedometer, flanked on the right by a combined fuel/temperature gauge and on the left by an instrument that imparts the novel statistic of the available percentage of engine power – a type of rev-counter in reverse, but much more discreet...

The electric gear selector is used to choose R, N, D, for Reverse, Neutral and Drive, on the enunciator but when manual pressure is removed, the selector reverts to its central position. For the 'Park' setting, the lever is pushed inwards. The door mirrors are mounted high and proud of the car, which provide an excellent view. The rear window is fairly large and, after allowing for the intrusion of the substantial headrests, the scope of the rear-view mirror is quite adequate. The indicators are operated with a conventional stalk on the left side of the steering column, although it does have one operational quirk. Push up for right and down for left but, if the driver wishes to manually cancel the signal, another push in the same direction is required. As with gear selection, a little thought is needed until these tasks become second nature.

The throttle pedal has a perfect balance and tension, which allows smooth and rapid acceleration. The transmission is configured to move quickly through the six ratios, when, once in top gear the low-speed torque of the engine can be used to maximum. This it does seamlessly. The Phantom really is one of those cars where the surrounding scenery appears to move past at an almost indecent rate compared to the efforts made by the driver and machine. The commanding position, excellent forward view, including the crest of both front wings and the apparently unlimited power combine for a driving experience second to none.

Narrow twisting lanes with pedestrians, dogs and horses cause no problem for the Phantom. The steering feel and gearing allow the driver to flick the car around obstacles in a sports car-like way, should they loom out of nowhere and emergency avoidance is needed. This feeling of security is aided by the computer-sensed air suspension that allows only a modicum of body roll and minimises the effect of G-force on driver and passenger. British A roads, where overtaking is possible, are the most fun with the Phantom, although one aspect does need getting used to: not only does the gearbox select top gear as soon as possible, but it stays there as long as possible when pressing the accelerator fully. This is to continue making use of the low-speed engine torque, but a new driver will wonder if the kickdown is working. In reality, the view outside the car will be slipping past quicker and quicker and the transmission will eventually drop a gear or two if 'emergency' acceleration is called for. Likewise, when easing off the throttle the available torque will defer a downwards gear change. All the while, the 'available power' dial shows 50-95 per cent still waiting to be unleashed.

Above and following pages: fast country roads really allow the Phantom to show its pedigree.

Who knows at what speed and how steep a gradient would be needed to drag the dial's needle to zero!

Potholes and other surface deficiencies are literally rendered inconsequential by the adaptive suspension system. The bump may be apparent but the car absorbs just about everything. Driver and passengers may hear a muffled thump, but they will feel nothing. The feedback to the steering wheel and the feeling of driver control are just about perfect. How Rolls-Royce has managed to isolate the more unpleasant aspects of poor road surfaces and yet retain such a dynamic feel to the steering is quite remarkable. Although no Formula 1 racing car, the engineers have found the perfect balance of control, performance and pampered luxury for the Phantom.

Any large luxury saloon should perform well on motorways; the surfaces are mostly good and the speed band predictable. Indeed, most cars do perform very well, so it is more difficult for the Phantom to shine here. But outstanding it is. Little wind or road noise is transmitted to the cabin and the car seems unaffected by crosswinds. The enormously powerful brakes can reduce speed in an astonishing manner and, of course, the steering and suspension continue to imbue a feeling of control in almost every situation. Cruise along at the 70mph British national speed limit and that 'Available Power' dial will show 90 per cent. It really is not a case of what the car does, but what it does not do that allows its occupants to enjoy the environment and the isolation from the world outside. Over the years, Rolls-Royce designers have demonstrated a clever knack of making their cars feel a great deal smaller than they actually are to the fortunate person at the helm. The Phantom continues this splendid achievement, which is more of an accomplishment than ever in the densely populated traffic of today. This and the other triumphs of the 'Driver Interface', as the company would say, make driving the Rolls-Royce Phantom a unique experience. For all the right reasons.

The hub of the matter: minimal instrumentation (above) is traditional and intuitive in design while leather textures and stitching in the Rolls-Royce are done to perfection (right).

GB
HX03 BWG

2 HOW BMW CAME TO COVET ROLLS-ROYCE

Apart from Rolls-Royce, most of the great marques had been taken over or were simply irrelevant when BMW decided to reach for the automotive stars

By the early years of the last century the motor vehicle had already superceded the horse-drawn to a large extent. (photo: The National Motor Museum)

When Henry Royce and Charles Rolls formed their famous partnership, there was a plethora of other motor car manufacturers. Great Britain, France, Germany and the United States were the principal countries in which these early cars were built. As is so often the case with many innovative developments, Britain's nascent car industry was hampered by ill-informed and reactionary politicians. In fact, but for the efforts of John Montagu, the second Baron Montagu of Beaulieu and father of the present Lord Edward Montagu, British motorists might still be driving at 4mph behind a man walking along carrying a red flag!

In 1896, it was Montagu, together with a small band of parliamentary supporters, who achieved the repeal of the 1865 Locomotives & Highways Act, which had been ill-advisedly concocted to protect horses and pedestrians. This had been amended in 1878 when the infamous red flag requirement was dropped (although the human advance party was still mandatory), but in 1896 Montagu and friends finally had cars legally recognised as 'light locomotives' if they weighed less than three tons, and the speed limit was raised to 12mph.

In 1900, the Prince of Wales took delivery of his first automobile and announced: "I shall make the motor car a necessity for every English gentleman." The addition of Royal patronage to the swelling ranks of motorists massively boosted the cause of the car, and it was not long before British entrepreneurs began, belatedly, to form an automotive industry.

Germany had no such early legislative straitjacket. In 1885, in Mannheim, Karl Benz successfully built and drove his first motor car. Indeed, it is widely accepted as being the world's first successful vehicle powered by an internal-combustion engine. The next year, in Bad Cannstatt near Stuttgart, Gottlieb Daimler and his partner Wilhelm Maybach built their first motor car. In 1902, their cars were sold under the brand name of Mercedes (named after the daughter of the company's French distributor Emile Jellinek). In 1926, these two pioneering organisations merged to become Daimler-Benz, while its cars were sold with 'Mercedes-Benz' badges. Many decades later in 1998, Daimler-Benz merged with the Chrysler Corporation to form DaimlerChrysler.

Wilhelm Maybach, however, had departed Daimler's company in 1907, to collaborate on aero engines with Count Zeppelin, mainly for the latter's airships. By 1921, Maybach was manufacturing powerful and highly luxurious cars on his own and, when production finally petered out in 1941, over 2000 cars had been produced. His company was still in business in 1960 making marine and railway engines, when Daimler-Benz took it over. All of the founders, of course, were long dead and so too, it seemed, was the Maybach car.

VAPOUR
BATHS
42 CORNHILL
LH 4529
LB-7705
LD 9723

Above: the Honourable John Douglas Scott Montagu (left) and the Prince of Wales, who would become King Edward VII, early motorists both, pictured with Montagu's 12hp Daimler at Highcliffe Castle in August 1899.

Meanwhile, Munich's Bayerische Flugzeug Werke had been formed in 1916, to make aero engines. In 1922, the name was changed to Bayerische Motoren Werke, and in 1923 the firm's first BMW motorcycle appeared. Five years later, BMW purchased the Eisenach Dixi car company, which produced the British Austin 7 under licence.

Now BMW was a carmaker too. The BMW Dixi was the first car to carry the famous stylised roundel that represents the white of a turning propeller against the blue of the sky. BMW established itself throughout the 1930s as building solid, dependable cars. Apart from the sporty 328 model, its cars initially struggled to achieve the enthusiastic following Mercedes-Benz enjoyed. After the Second World War and a complex, politically enforced liaison with Britain's Bristol Car Company, production in Munich restarted in 1952 with the 501 range. Bubble cars were introduced in 1955 to boost the company's flagging turnover as the 501 and other large cars struggled to find buyers. Yet the 1956 507 sports car, with V8 engine and stunningly attractive styling, was an instant classic, despite selling in small numbers.

By 1959, BMW was in a parlous financial state, but a rescue bid was made by industrialist Herbert Quandt, whose surviving family members together still exercise a controlling stake in the company. He instigated a change of direction which resulted in BMW focusing on the emerging market for practical saloon cars with an emphasis on neat styling and a sporty flavour.

The first of these was the 1500 of 1962 – the basis from which all of BMW's saloon car ranges are descended to this day. From that time forward, the company has gone from strength to strength and yet, unlike other carmakers, has stubbornly refused to conform to the car industry norm. It has continued to manufacture, for example, both motorcycles and aircraft engines. Intriguingly, BMW has a reputation for constantly rising profitability; all its cars, moreover, have been cleverly and attractively designed, and beautifully engineered.

Above: the revived Maybach, created by DaimlerChrysler, in the company of one of the 2000 or so examples of the marque built before the Second World War.

Right: it looked like an Austin Seven because that is exactly what it was. This 1928 Dixi, BMW's very first car, was a German-made version of the British economy car.

BMW could have chosen another venerable marque like Napier (this is a 40/50hp model from the early 1920s) to rejuvenate, but nothing available had the contemporary relevance of Rolls-Royce.

Consolidation in the car industry began long ago. Today, over 90 per cent of the cars manufactured globally come from just 10 large companies or close alliances and, as the world has a manufacturing overcapacity for new cars estimated at about 30 per cent, a further reduction of independent companies is likely. BMW is a comparatively small company, but being a big player in the rarefied world of quality cars is less exposed to this overcapacity.

For a decade or more, the sellers of mass-produced automobiles have slowly bought up any available surviving smaller companies whose names are associated with quality cars. Saab fell to General Motors; Aston Martin, Jaguar and Land Rover to Ford; Bentley, Bugatti and Lamborghini to Volkswagen. It remains to be seen if this raises the perception of quality within the parent groups or devalues the same for the bespoke brands they now incorporate.

Despite suffering years of insufficient financial backing during the second half of the last century, the engineers at Rolls-Royce had continued to turn out a very good product against the odds. It was good enough to maintain the Rolls-Royce name and world-famous mascot as, respectively, a byword and symbol of engineering excellence. This alone made it the glittering prize in an era of shrinking takeover opportunities, and one which BMW set its heart upon. This was despite BMW's previous foray into the British motor industry with the acquisition of Rover in 1994. This did not work out well – Rover proved an unwilling patient for BMW's special kind of corporate medicine. However, BMW strongly believed that there was an opportunity for a spectacular rejuvenation of Rolls-Royce.

Bearing in mind an already established technical co-operation that BMW enjoyed with Rolls-Royce Motor Cars, as well as the aero engine joint-venture between BMW and Rolls-Royce plc in BMW Rolls-Royce GmbH, the German carmaker was well placed to make a sensible bid for the company when it eventually came on the market.

The acquisition process was tortuous and lengthy, and is covered in detail in the next chapter. However, once Rolls-Royce enthusiasts understood that BMW really was to be the new custodian of Rolls-Royce, its faith in the German company's ethos of the highest quality was reinforced. Based on BMW's impeccable credentials built up over the last 40 years, the takeover also reassured Rolls-Royce customers that the brand had been delivered into safe hands.

Of course, had it failed, BMW could have tried to acquire another name steeped in the history of superb quality cars of distinction: Isotta-Fraschini, Hispano-Suiza, Duesenberg, Pierce Arrow or Napier are all examples of venerable names that could conceivably have been obtained. Yet they all have the same enormous disadvantage: they have all been defunct for at least 50 years. No-one really remembers them except old car enthusiasts. Rolls-Royce, and Bentley, were the

BMW took out a licence to manufacture the Italian Isetta in 1955; this economical 'bubble car' proved a lucrative hit across Europe.

The BMW 501 of 1952 was a fine car in many ways, but it struggled to find enough customers in the post-war period to secure BMW's survival.

The BMW 1500 of 1962 was the foundation of BMW's present-day success, tapping into demand for sporty executive cars for the motorway age.

The delectable BMW 507 sports car of 1955 sold in small numbers despite its attractive styling and vivid V8 performance.

only available luxury brands with a history of continuous production still to hold their places at the top of the automotive tree. Most people in the Western world have, arguably, a reasonable understanding of what Rolls-Royce in particular stands for.

Daimler-Benz had also hoped to grab Rolls-Royce before its close German competitor. But after that possibility was finally denied, it had to revert to its 'plan B'. Daimler-Benz had toyed with the idea of reviving Maybach for decades, just as, industry insiders reckon, Volkswagen planned to dust off the old Horch name had it been unable to get its hands on Bentley, Rolls-Royce's long-term stablemate. Now the time was right to press the 'Maybach button' (no matter how arcane the connotations were for Maybach outside Germany in the 21st century) in Daimler-Benz's attempt to produce a super-saloon superior even to the already excellent Mercedes-Benz S-Class.

To outsiders in 2004, it would appear to be a bold and adventurous scheme. Except for one fact: no-one is waiting to see if the Rolls-Royce Phantom can live up to and beat the Maybach – everybody is wondering if the Maybach can match the Rolls-Royce. Such is the value of continuous production for 100 years. The Maybach may be in direct competition with the Phantom; both cars are large and very expensive, and both are in the old-fashioned tradition of 'grand routiers', but they are likely to attract very different customers.

The Maybach is, in essence, and even basic profile, an enlarged Mercedes but with a good deal more luxury options available than any other car DaimlerChrysler can muster; the rear seating is reminiscent of the first-class accommodation in a long-range jet aircraft. The Rolls-Royce boasts less in the way of super-luxurious options; the rear seating here is more intimate, as might be found inside the immaculately furnished London apartment of an English gentleman and his wife. It is a case of horses for courses – or even lifestyles – but BMW wanted to take on Rolls-Royce precisely because of what these fine British cars have always stood for, and not simply as a 'name' to be added to a corporate trophy cabinet.

One small but interesting historical footnote should be added. Fahrzeug Fabrik Eisenach AG, the company BMW took over to produce the Dixi Austin 7, produced until 1904 petrol engined cars sold under the name Wartburg. These cars were in fact French Decauvilles built under licence. Coincidentally, it was the purchase of a second-hand Decauville in 1902 that inspired Frederick Henry Royce to try and improve this adequate but typically (for the time) imperfect little twin-cylinder car.

Who would have thought that the maker of the Decauville would have been the initial inspiration for two great engineering companies, separated by international boundaries and 100 years, to join forces and produce a contender for the title of 'The Best Car In The World'?

Main picture: the gradual evolution of BMW's staple executive model, the 5 Series. Examples from 1972, 1981, 1988, 1995 and 2003.

Right: stylish coupes (right to left) 328, 503, 3200CS, 3.0CSi and 6 Series, with the 8 Series in the foreground.

3 BACKGROUND TO 'THE DEAL'

Much have I travelled in the realms of gold, and many goodly states and kingdoms seen – JOHN KEATS

Main picture: Henry Royce, the company co-founder and technical perfectionist who was knighted for his engineering work.

Inset: Royce's partner, the Honourable Charles Rolls, who was killed in an air crash in Bournemouth in 1910.

During the 100 years the Rolls-Royce car has been produced, there have been four occasions when the motoring public has perceived the success of the car and the future of its manufacturer to be in possible jeopardy. These were the death of Charles Rolls, the death of Henry Royce, the financial crisis at Rolls-Royce in the early 1970s and the complexity of Rolls-Royce's change of ownership as the 20th century came to an end. Nonetheless, the Rolls-Royce marque has survived, and this is the story of how.

In June 1910, the Honourable Charles Rolls died in a flying accident at the Bournemouth Air Show. He was only 32, but had been instrumental in establishing Rolls-Royce motor cars as the chosen transport for the aristocratic and rich of Great Britain and its Empire. In truth, by the day of his death, Rolls was expending very little effort on the business of Rolls-Royce Ltd. His passion for flying and aircraft design had become all-embracing. Despite this untimely loss to the company, the design and engineering excellence of Frederick Henry Royce and the skill of his workforce, both blue and white-collar, ensured rising sales figures. The established quality of the 40/50hp, by then widely called 'The Silver Ghost', bore witness to this.

Sir Henry Royce survived his co-founder by 23 years, dying aged 70 on 22 April 1933. By then, the well-established company had a 'talent pool' large enough to withstand the loss of Royce – arguably the greatest automotive designer and engineer of his time. By 1933, he had overseen the introduction of the Phantom II, the smaller 20/25hp, and even the 3.5 litre Bentley that expanded Rolls-Royce's customer base by catering for more sporting owners. Royce's talents had also made the company a leading manufacturer of aero engines, his last major design being the Model R, which powered the Supermarine-built aircraft that won the Schneider Trophy in 1929 and 1931.

Royce had established an all-pervading culture of teamwork and this legacy, plus superior, continual refinement of engineering design, successfully carried the company right through to the 1960s. The more prudent financial control instigated soon after his demise certainly cemented Rolls-Royce's sound financial grounding. But by 1971, the company's fastidious culture was in crisis.

Thanks to the Second Word War, the aero engine division had long overshadowed the car-making side, but development costs of its new RB211 turbofan power unit were spiralling by the close of the 1960s. In order to boost its power to satisfy Lockheed, a key customer, 10 per cent of its 4500 components were being redesigned every month. The expense was colossal, yet the company's accounting system failed to show the full picture so, to worldwide amazement, on 4 February

The controversial frontal aspect of the new Phantom has divided opinion but is unmistakably Rolls-Royce.

Opposite: the traditional Rolls-Royce badge, and side indicator in close up, showing the superlative fit of even the smallest components.

1971 Rolls-Royce went into receivership. The stricken company was quickly nationalised to guarantee supplies of engines for military purposes, but a giant question mark hovered over the car division.

At the Crewe, Cheshire headquarters, managers pondered cancelling a range of mildly updated two-door coachbuilt models but, rather than waste all the effort ploughed into their design, the 'new' Corniche (this more evocative name replaced Silver Shadow) drophead and fixedhead models were introduced defiantly to the media just four weeks after Rolls-Royce's insolvency was revealed. Journalists who drove the cars at their launch on the Corniche roads between Nice and Monte Carlo were unanimously supportive and, by May 1973, a limited company, Rolls-Royce Motors Ltd., had been formed and floated on the London Stock Exchange to continue production of Rolls-Royce and Bentley motor cars. The potential corporate disaster had been weathered successfully.

Defence manufacturer Vickers decided to make what became a successful bid for Rolls-Royce Motor Cars in 1980, and the new Silver Spirit (codenamed SZ) range of cars was launched. But this was a time of high taxation, low profits and constant oil crises, and many observers were disappointed the new model was so similar in size and weight to its predecessor – an inevitability because it was constructed on the old Silver Shadow chassis and floorpan to save money. This was hardly a car for the many people to whom 'belt-tightening' was paramount. The 1980s and 1990s were decades of economic feast and famine but production of the SZ range continued even if it did not increase much. The Bentley derivatives quickly rose in popularity; sadly, at the expense of Rolls-Royce orders, not those of rival manufacturers like Mercedes-Benz and Jaguar. As a consequence, Rolls-Royce Motor Cars' contribution to the parent company's profits was negligible, and Vickers was tempted to sell off such an underperforming asset

ROLLS
ROYCE

A rare opportunity to absorb the entire, imposing side profile of the Phantom in this studio study, amply demonstrating the subtlety of the styling.

on its balance sheet, especially when BMW and Toyota both showed interest in buying the carmaker.

Instead, though, Vickers decided to haul Rolls-Royce back into the black. The labour force was reduced substantially from 5500 employees in the 1980s to 3000 by 1991. Serious problems of quality control and outdated systems were addressed, and BMW was contracted to improve the body rigidity. Experts from Munich were soon advising on matters ranging from paint technology to air-conditioning systems.

It was a comfortable relationship, progressing steadily towards an all-new model. Rolls-Royce chief executive, Peter Ward, and BMW's board member for research and development, Dr. Wolfgang Reitzle, worked well together, but Reitzle was completely unaware that Ward was secretly negotiating a deal for new engines with Helmut Werner, CEO of the Mercedes-Benz AG. Rolls-Royce's own superb but ancient 6.75 litre V8 engine needed urgent replacement. Naturally, to be the supplier of that substitute would be a tremendous 'foot in the door' for Daimler-Benz, but also a potential prize on the list of parts supplied by its deadly rival, BMW. Vickers supported Ward's twin negotiations because they saw the benefit of competition, although

Ward favoured the Mercedes-built V8 and V12 engines as the best engineering solution.

In May 1993, Dr. Bernd Pischetsrieder, a brilliant engineer with a deep understanding of the importance of branding, took over as head of BMW's board of management, and immediately began to build a relationship with Vickers chairman Sir Colin Chandler. A year later, Peter Ward promised Helmut Werner that Daimler-Benz would be the chosen engine supplier for the SZ Series engine replacement. Meanwhile, however, BMW was hard at work on body and subframe development for this very same new range. On 14 December, Sir Colin Chandler visited Sir Ralph Robins, chairman of aero engine maker Rolls-Royce plc, to see how he felt about Daimler-Benz supplying the new car's engines. Sir Ralph was vehemently against it because Rolls-Royce plc had enjoyed a long working relationship with BMW – the two were partners in a project to develop a new generation of medium-sized fan jet engines, and in direct competition with a Daimler-Benz subsidiary. Still, why should Vickers be so concerned with gaining the blessing of a company now totally unconnected with the motor industry?

This was because Rolls-Royce plc held the trademarks to the name, the radiator shell design and the linked R-R insignia. Sir Colin was aware that a long legal battle over those rights could seriously jeopardise the launch of the new car, and it was a risk he did not wish to take. Peter Ward was instructed to cease negotiations with Daimler-Benz, a command that marked the start of a rift between him and Sir Colin. The split became final during a press conference where it was revealed that Cosworth Engineering would supply Rolls-Royce Motor Cars with turbochargers for V8 and, intriguingly, V12 engines. The announcement was made jointly by Chandler, Ward, Bernd Pischetsrieder and Chris Woodwark, head of Cosworth. After the press conference, they all enjoyed a celebratory lunch at Vickers' offices, with the exception of Peter Ward. He had gone home without a job.

Chris Woodwark took over as chief executive of Rolls-Royce Motor Cars in the winter of 1994. He soon discovered the company's development engineers were not confident they had the expertise to design all the systems required by the new car that would replace the SZ range. So BMW's Pischetsrieder agreed to help set up the production facilities at Crewe, with special attention to air-conditioning, electronics, air bags and seat design. By then, BMW was responsible for over 30 per cent of the development of what eventually became the Rolls-Royce Silver Seraph and Bentley Arnage, and therefore for steering the British marque's destiny.

Graham Morris, lately of Audi and a relative newcomer at Rolls-Royce, superseded Woodwark as chief executive in March 1997, only to discover seven months later that Vickers had put Rolls-Royce up for sale without consulting or informing the management or workers. On 10 November, BMW announced its interest in buying the company, followed two weeks later by Volkswagen's Dr. Ferdinand Piech, grandson of Dr. Ferdinand Porsche, declaring in the business newspaper *Handelsblatt* that Vickers had already made a deal with VW. A consortium of British 'enthusiasts', with a small 'e' (as opposed to a team endorsed by the Rolls-Royce Enthusiasts' Club) also declared an interest, but this group, perhaps led by hearts rather than heads, eventually crumbled under the pressure of internal squabbling.

All this time, the SZ range had been continually developed but, by 1997, had reached the end of its viable lifespan. It was now time for the Silver Seraph to take the baton. The styling of the Silver Seraph was pure Rolls-Royce but, whereas the SZ's bodyshell was provided by an outside supplier, now complete major 'organs' such as the engine and the air-conditioning system were delivered ready to be dropped straight into the car. And the supplier's name was BMW.

The Silver Seraph was launched at the 1998 Geneva motor show, and meanwhile Daimler-Benz retired from the contest, deciding instead to compete with Rolls-Royce by resurrecting the Maybach name on an all-new car. On 23 March, Sir Colin Chandler met with VW's Ferdinand Piech and sales and marketing director, Dr. Robert Büchelhofer. They offered £320 million for Rolls-Royce Motor Cars on condition that rights to the name were included.

The following day, Büchelhofer visited Sir Ralph Robins, who explained that Rolls-Royce plc still held all the trademarks from before the 1971 split of the aero-engine and motor divisions. On 25 March, BMW made a counter offer of £340 million, a promise to invest a further £1 billion in the business and an increase in the workforce to 5,000. Soon afterwards, all of this had the blessing of Rolls-Royce plc together with the crucial agreement for the transfer of the trademarks to BMW. There followed a month of negotiating which resulted in Vickers agreeing the sale, in principle, to BMW.

Almost immediately, VW increased its offer to £430 million with no special conditions, and a promise of an investment of £1.5 billion in the company so that 10,000 cars could be produced annually. In essence, Vickers had used the BMW offer as a lever to force VW to take on the same contract, but for an extra £90 million, and all this was too much for Vickers to deny its shareholders. Pischetsrieder saw the deal was slipping away from BMW, and he took radical action. He advised all interested parties that if another car manufacturer

A radical new look for Rolls-Royce has quickly gained acceptance from even the most traditional enthusiasts of the marque.

GWD 968

was to buy Rolls-Royce Motor Cars, subject to all contractual obligations, the supply of expertise and components to the new Seraph/Arnage would end.

Over the Whitsun weekend of 1998, the BMW board met at the London headquarters of HSBC. Pischetsrieder's representative put forward a proposal to buy the whole of Vickers plc for £1 billion. Sir Ralph Robins was consulted, and a plan was formalised. HSBC would finance the purchase. The military side of Vickers would be sold off and Rolls-Royce plc would take a share in the action at Rolls-Royce Motor Cars. At the 11th hour, however, Rolls-Royce plc pulled out and, although the financing was still in place, BMW decided against the sole ownership of Vickers.

Two weeks later, Vickers held an extraordinary general meeting where VW's offer to purchase Rolls-Royce Motor Cars was accepted. The deal was sealed shortly afterwards but then VW's lawyers indulged in some buyer's remorse: what had they actually contracted to purchase? Who had which trademarks? And what were the actual 'contractual obligations' BMW would or would not honour? True to its word, BMW confirmed that supplies of components and expertise would cease one year from VW's purchase of Rolls-Royce Motor Cars. Piech knew that, without BMW components, the Seraph and Arnage models could not be produced in a commercially viable manner. He would have to negotiate a deal with Pischetsrieder if new Rolls-Royce cars were not to disappear for a long period, all but abandoning their loyal clientele.

Early in the morning of 28 July, a meeting took place in the clubhouse of the Neuburg an der Donau golf course, close to the Audi headquarters at Ingolstadt, Germany. Piech and Pischetsrieder were joined by the head of VW's supervisory board of management, Dr. Klaus Liesen, and his BMW counterpart, Dr. Eberhard von Kuenheim. Also present were the head of the state of Lower Saxony, Gerhard Schröder – soon to become German Chancellor – and the Prime Minister of Bavaria, Dr. Edmund Stoiber. The basis of an agreement was thrashed out, in which VW agreed to pay Vickers DM 1 billion for the Rolls-Royce factory at Crewe along with the rights to the Bentley trademarks. The party then drove to a nearby airbase for further discussions. Only VW-built Audis were used for transport to the airbase, something BMW negotiators would only agree to if the planned follow-up trip from Heathrow to London was undertaken in BMWs.

It would be some time before the VW team realised BMW had outsmarted them with a publicity coup. The Audi drive was undertaken secretly, away from the public gaze; the BMW motorcade, meanwhile, was in full view of the world's press and TV, as was the press conference to announce the agreed deal for which they had come to London.

Sir Ralph Robins of Rolls-Royce plc received his guests and shook hands with Piech and Pischetsrieder on a three-way agreement. BMW would pay Rolls-Royce plc £40 million for the rights to all the Rolls-Royce trademarks. BMW in turn would agree to continue supplying components to VW for the Silver Seraph and Bentley Arnage range of cars for as long as they remained in production. VW would acquire the Crewe factory and the Bentley trademarks outright. It would also have the benefit of the continued use of the Rolls-Royce trademarks until 31 December 2002. Thereafter, the Rolls-Royce trademarks would transfer to BMW, which could market a Rolls-Royce car from 1 January 2003.

At first sight, it seemed BMW had the advantage with the control of necessary supplies for the current range of cars. In reality, Volkswagen, with the purchase of Rolls-Royce Motor Cars Ltd., had taken rights to some of the trademarks not vested with Rolls-Royce plc; namely the Spirit of Ecstasy mascot and certain model names such as Continental that had been used on both Rolls-Royce and Bentley cars in the past. Piech knew just as well as Pischetsrieder how necessary these would be to anyone producing a new Rolls-Royce car, but Sir Ralph Robins saw to it that the iconic Spirit of Ecstasy was not denied to BMW. Rolls-Royce plc also agreed to lend back to BMW the £40 million to help finance the building of a new manufacturing plant. At the time of this meeting, Goodwood had not yet been chosen.

Two days later, Graham Morris resigned from his position as chief executive at Rolls-Royce Motor Cars Ltd. He had previously given his word to the workforce that Rolls-Royce and Bentley would stay together while he was in charge. His position was taken by long-time Rolls-Royce man Tony Gott, but as caretaker chief executive. Despite his dexterous handling of the acquisition of the rights to produce future Rolls-Royce cars, Bernd Pischetsrieder was soon fired from BMW – for his involvement in another Anglo-German venture: the ill-starred BMW takeover of Rover. But remembering

How close does this, the Phantom, come to the ideas of the company directors who forged the deal?

that old business adage that there is no profit in revenge, VW offered Pischetsrieder – the man who had outwitted them – the job of running its Seat subsidiary, eventually leading to his heading the VW group.

There was still one bitter pill for BMW to swallow. In all the wrangling, one important item had been giving concern to Pischetsrieder and his team. Since 1947, Rolls-Royce had owned a magnificent 1907 40/50hp car, chassis number 60551, known as the Silver Ghost, or more often by its registration number AX 201. It was not included in the Rolls-Royce assets to BMW, so ironically Volkswagen now possesses probably the world's most famous and valuable Rolls-Royce!

For BMW, Project Rolls-Royce had become a reality. But everything that had happened was merely a prelude to the real work of designing and building a brand new car worthy of carrying the Spirit of Ecstasy mascot. BMW knew it had one chance to make a success of this venture and, at this point, it did not even have anywhere to build the car. BMW would never be forgiven for failing to meet the expectations of Rolls-Royce owners, the motoring press or, indeed, the general public, which holds the famous British name close to its heart. This Rolls-Royce had to earn, without compromise, the sobriquet 'The Best Car in the World' like no other before.

4 PHANTOM PHILOSOPHY

Strive for perfection in everything you do. Take the best that exists and make it better. When it doesn't exist, design it – SIR HENRY ROYCE

Above: Karl-Heinz Kalbfell, the head of Project Rolls-Royce.

Opposite: a haunting image of Phantoms lined up and ready to meet their proud new owners.

During the summer of 1998, all the key personnel were being recruited to undertake the design work on the Project Rolls-Royce car. Codenamed RR01, it would eventually become the new Phantom. Karl-Heinz Kalbfell, in charge of brand and product strategy at BMW, was appointed to take overall responsibility for Project Rolls-Royce. Karl Baumer, who had worked at BMW since 1981 was one of the first to join Kalbfell's tight-knit team. In 1997, he had been asked to make the case for Rolls-Royce if either the Crewe plant or the brand were acquired and, after the negotiations had been completed in 1998, he was given the task of creating a business plan for Rolls-Royce together with a future model policy.

To do this, Baumer and his colleague Ulrich Knieps visited the world's leading dealerships to "get the brand feel and customer profiles and their expectations." He was ready to present his findings to the BMW board in December, and the following month it met to consider the proposed direction. The decision was made to press ahead with a 'Phantom'-type car.

Baumer explains: "All types of car were considered but the Phantom became the natural choice. Once you considered all the requirements such as the flat floor, the rear seating and the coach doors, together with all the other needs of a true Rolls-Royce, then the only type of car that could be built without compromise would be one like the Phantom. Car design is a matter of convergence. On the one hand, the designers want to make a coupe that no one can sit in. On the other hand, the engineers want to make a car in which everyone can wear a top hat. The convergence of these two groups is where the saleable car is." An important point emerged at this early stage. RR01 would be a car to complement an owner's lifestyle – a car that would be fitting.

This was by no means the end of Karl Baumer's involvement with the project. In the summer of 1999, he was sent to find an appropriate site for a new Rolls-Royce manufacturing plant and head office; and when that quest had been successfully completed, he began his primary job as head of engineering for Project Rolls-Royce. Karl-Heinz Kalbfell was not a man to let the seeds of managerial talent remain in only one furrow.

Kalbfell made it quite clear to his BMW colleagues that this car would only succeed if its design was absolutely uncompromised by established BMW policies. He knew concepts and features that made perfect solutions on a BMW would not necessarily work for RR01. After all, the car was to be sold in a market sector not catered to by any BMW car. Baumer found in his extensive research that potential Rolls-Royce buyers simply would not contemplate the purchase of a car adapted from a large BMW, such as the 7 Series. New thinking had to flourish and every influential BMW

ROLLS
RR
ROYCE

A Phantom driving through London's West End; Karl-Heinz Kalbfell and his team felt it was essential that the car should be designed in the city.

figure, including the Quandt family members who own 40 per cent of the Bavarian company, was firmly behind the project. That rock-solid confidence allowed Kalbfell to create a separate division for the marque. Of course, BMW's entire range of research facilities and expertise were available and used when appropriate, but 'separate' thinking needed 'separate' premises, and these were soon found.

Everyone agreed with Kalbfell that the design centre should be in London, an important Rolls-Royce 'heartland' with its high concentration of owners, historic backdrop and links to the marque's great coachbuilders. To assemble its design team, BMW tapped its worldwide pool of design talent from Munich, from its Designworks studios in California, and from the Rover and Land-Rover organisations in Britain that BMW then owned.

In January 1999, the entire design team moved into rented accommodation, which became known as 'The Bank': two floors of a building on the corner of Bayswater Road and Elms Mews, on the north side of London's Hyde Park. It was charming, with an abundance of eccentricities thanks to its former life as a bank; it even featured a spiral staircase. It was a long way from the almost scientific approach of BMW in Munich, both in distance and ambience. Ideas could flourish here without the undue intrusion of the BMW ethos.

Chief designer Ian Cameron, on the right, makes a point about the Phantom to his colleagues.

When the Bank ran out of space in May 1999, further premises were rented at a film studio three miles away in Holborn, codenamed 'The Bookshop' after a nearby business. Here, each of the three exterior designs was transformed into two-fifths-size clay models, big enough for analysis but small enough for rapid adjustments, and handling. The workforce gave the project a codename: Roger Rabbit. Under the agreement with Volkswagen, no external use of the name Rolls-Royce or trademarks were allowed by BMW before January 2003. Hence, any use of the letters RR would refer only to the codename.

The Bank team consisted of five competing designers of which three were exterior designers and two were interior designers. BMW director of design Chris Bangle chose Ian Cameron as the project's chief designer. Cameron had graduated in Vehicle Design from London's Royal College of Art and subsequently spent six years working for Pininfarina in Italy, where he learnt the additional discipline of working with build drawings instead of clay models.

"In Italy, they do proper construction drawings of the surfaces," he explains. "They then make those as sections and fill them in. It trains you to think in a completely different way. You think three-dimensionally on a two-dimensional piece of paper. I am very grateful for my training in that background."

After a spell with Fiat's commercial vehicle division IVECO, Cameron joined BMW in 1992 to run the exterior design programme of the 3 Series. Later, he worked on the Z8 roadster and the L30 project – which became the latest Range Rover. Cameron feels his work

Interior designer Charles Coldham (second from right) describes a concept to other members of the design team.

on this quintessentially British, Land-Rover-built car, along with his experience of spaceframe technology (of which more later) with the Z8, made him a good choice for RR01. BMW also needed someone with a good cultural understanding of London, a natural habitat for Rolls-Royce cars that is also Cameron's home city.

"I supported the move away from BMW facilities," he says. "It's a bit like going on holiday; you don't do the same things as when you are at home. The greater effort of having to set up something entirely new triggers changes in your thinking. You can work from a clean sheet of paper without needing to fit in with existing parameters."

An outsider could therefore be forgiven for thinking the RR01 team wanted to have nothing to do with the parent company in Munich. In fact, the truth was the complete opposite. While maintaining its decision-making autonomy, the team would draw substantially on BMW's expertise in terms of both engineering and design. Cameron's knowledge gained in the design genesis of the Z8 sports car would prove a vital stepping stone on the way to designing the Phantom's aluminium 'spaceframe' inner structure – the largest ever envisaged for a motor car. The intrinsic adaptability of a BMW V12 engine also proved an excellent basis for the re-engineered power unit the Phantom required. And there was no better source for manufacturing the

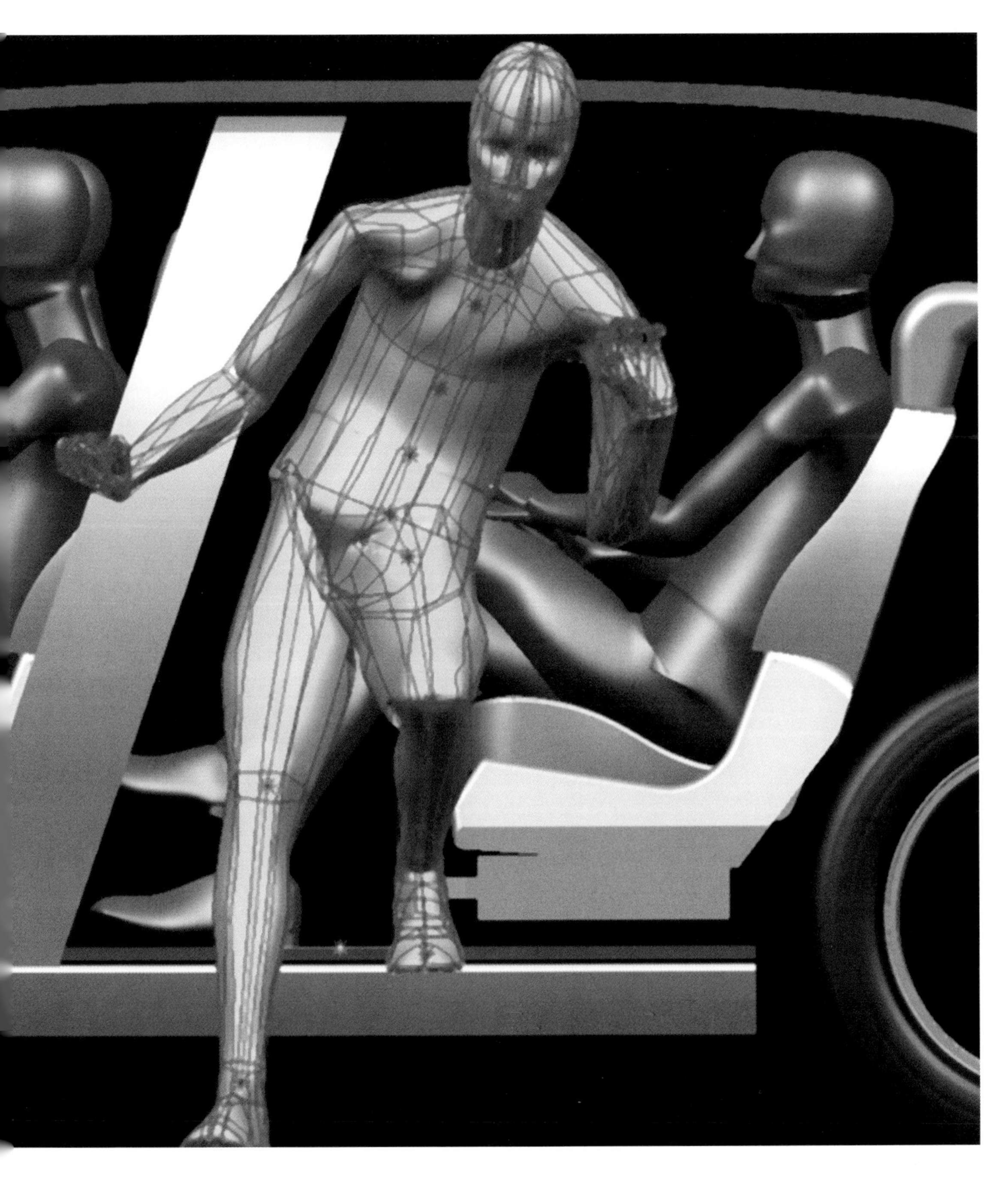

A computer-generated passenger enjoys easy egress from the Phantom's rear coach door.

ready-for-paint bodies than BMW's Dingolfing body shop. Certainly, it was pointlessly expensive to replicate this facility on a smaller scale for Rolls-Royce alone.

Perhaps, in a slight case of the tail wagging the dog, the members of Project Rolls-Royce took this view which was described by chief engineer, Dr. Tim Leverton. "The strategy was to build on and exploit the competencies of the whole BMW group within a framework of targets and demands orientated directly towards the Rolls-Royce marque." BMW was comfortable with this arrangement, and its hopes for a symbiotic relationship were rapidly becoming reality. It would be a few months before Rolls-Royce's key players could demonstrate the true synergy of the carefully constructed relationship, but demonstrate it they would.

Everyone who worked at the Bank became deeply immersed in the culture of Rolls-Royce. Ian Cameron is embarrassed to admit, after all his years at BMW: "At the end of the day, I knew infinitely more about Rolls-Royce than I ever did about BMW, and I am still learning." For the Bank team, this was not the straightforward task of designing a new car; this was an opportunity to re-establish a Rolls-Royce car as truly being the best in the world, and their enthusiasm alone was going to make this happen.

Cameron is unable to credit one single person at the Bank for the car's final design. He is pleased by the fact that the group worked as a team, without the cliques and personality clashes one might expect from such a closed environment with a time pressure to perform. Perhaps, in retrospect, if any two people could be congratulated for the success of the design project, it would probably be Chris Bangle, overall BMW design chief, whose decision it was to let the team continue without BMW interference, and Karl-Heinz Kalbfell, for his unwavering dedication in overseeing the process development as he envisioned it.

A philosophy for the car itself began to emerge. It would have to exhibit traditional Rolls-Royce proportions and use 21st century engineering solutions. It would first and foremost be designed around the needs of its occupants. The values and ideas that shaped this became known as the 'Authority Concept'. It was developed primarily to give both driver and passengers the ultimate feeling of well-being within the car. The positioning, the look and the feel of every item an occupant would come in contact with would be part of the Authority Concept. The seats should be the ultimate in comfort. Heating or entertainment controls would be intuitively placed, and side-window demisting would afford a condensation-free view. Even the space in the cabin was planned in the best Goldilocks tradition – 'not too big and not too small, but just right'. The 'Authority Concept' is entwined around all aspects of the car, but to expand upon it further at this point would only pre-empt later chapters.

Barker-bodied Phantom II shows its 'waftability' line picked out in red by Rolls-Royce design staff.

Exterior designer Marek Djordjevic was influenced by this magnificent Phantom II and its brightwork.

Typically, Rolls-Royce coachwork starts boldly at the front, and becomes 'softer' towards the rear.

The archetypal Rolls-Royce exterior design principle demonstrated. As the red marks show, body height has generally been twice the road wheel diameter.

Above: a classic coach door has right-angled corners which, when allied to a flat floor, allows supremely easy entry and exit.

Above right: vertical elements of the Silver Cloud's wings harmonise beautifully with the upright radiator grille.

Right: a Silver Wraith proves the case for the excellent proportions of a widening 'C' pillar and coach door.

Above: Ian Cameron listens to John Blatchley, the respected designer of the earlier Silver Cloud and Silver Shadow.

Opposite left: head of Project Rolls-Royce, Karl-Heinz Kalbfell (on right) chats with chief engineer Dr. Tim Leverton.

Opposite right: Karl Baumer, director of engineering, enthusiastically imparts wisdom.

When driver and passenger requirements had been assessed, the size of the finished RR01 and its engineering solutions, could be finalised. Although extremely important, the varying demands of the wind tunnel, the production engineers, and the usual motor industry financial constraints would be secondary considerations. As it turned out, the car needed to be about a fifth larger than is usual for a luxury saloon: RR01 was referred to as a '120 per cent car'.

Ian Cameron realised that over the years Rolls-Royce cars had shared several distinctive features: a long wheelbase with a short front overhang (the distance from the front wheel to the front tip of the car), a long rear overhang (the distance from the back of the rear wheel to the tail end of the car), and a long bonnet and large wheels that, including tyres, had a diameter about half the height of the overall car. All of these features are incorporated in the Phantom.

As before, at the rear of the car, the roofline blends into a wide 'C' pillar (the rearmost of the car's three vertical roof support posts) with the side profile essentially 'broad-shouldered'. A vertical upright front, dominated by the classic radiator grille and mascot, would give the finishing touch to the car's presence. Ian Cameron sums it up: "Our absolute priority was to create a motor car that is clearly a Rolls-Royce even when the radiator grille is not in view. More than this, the new car has to stand apart from all others."

Almost 100 years ago, *The Autocar* magazine described riding in a Rolls-Royce Silver Ghost as 'the feeling of being wafted through the countryside'. Soon afterwards, the company's engineers at its Nightingale Road, Derby works coined the word 'waftability' to describe the very essence of the Silver Ghost. RR01 would need mechanical components that would also endow it with 'waftability'. Subtle styling accents to emphasise this philosophy are best described by quoting a Project Rolls-Royce internal document. 'Waftability', it says, 'defines the smooth, resolute performance of the engine and driveline. It is manifested in the design by a long graceful line running along the sill of the Phantom. This line gently rises as your eye moves from the rear to the front, visualising a motor yacht at speed. An accent line of brightwork ties the classic Rolls-Royce radiator grille and long bonnet to the passenger cabin – like the reins of a horse to a carriage, the source of the

power and the driver are connected. This brightwork serves as a discreet but dynamic element of the design, not merely ornamentation'.

The waftability factor stems from the engine, its quietness and the way in which it delivers power. The older BMW 12-cylinder unit was not suitable. It was supplied to the old Rolls-Royce Motor Cars for the Silver Seraph, and was not popular in that role. The torque curve was such that the engine speed had to be relatively high to make use of the power available. Not a bad facet for a sporting saloon such as a BMW 7 Series, but inappropriate for a Rolls-Royce. A totally new engine was developed for the Phantom which has few design similarities to the current BMW V12 engine. The historic Rolls-Royce engine capacity of 6.75 litres delivered an adequate amount of silent power in just the required manner.

Whatever the stylists produced, they would have to take into consideration two immutable features: the Spirit of Ecstasy mascot and the Parthenon-style radiator shell. Not only would they be demanded by new owners, but the linked R-R badge and the name of the car were really all BMW had purchased. Ian Cameron joked that "it sometimes felt as if we had only paid for a mascot and a tarnished radiator grille." Rolls-Royce had spent too many years living off the memory of great cars but the unique identity was always, and would remain, the quintessential benchmark of automotive excellence.

All the Project Rolls-Royce team members had to supply was a car worthy of that accolade but they had only one chance to do it.

THE BANK DIARY

Project administrator Sally Young recorded the progress of the design of RR01 at the Bank in a diary, which has since become a historic Rolls-Royce document. It gives an insight into the camaraderie and dynamics of the design group working at the Bank, as it chronicles the research undertaken into the 'world' of prospective owners – particularly the opulent, sea-loving ones that would influence the car's design team. These are some of Sally's words.

Charles Coldham, whose interior design was chosen, peruses some early options.

FRIDAY, 12 MARCH 1999

The team make a slow journey out of London to P&A Wood in Essex. We are greeted courteously by Paul Wood and then given a tour of their extensive workshop in which everything is spick and span, and has us with mouths open and jaws dropping at the quality of their workmanship and the calibre of the cars on which they work. King Hussein of Jordan's first Rolls-Royce is there – the one in which he drove himself to and from Cambridge University. The team are allowed to photograph details and inspect everything. There is an exceptionally rare 4.5 litre blower Bentley, an Alfa Romeo 8C 2900 Superleggera and a Bentley R-type Continental.

In the showroom, a Phantom V causes much exclamation: the quality of the wood and the workmanship in the interior, the solidity and construction of the doors, the leather front seats and the specially-woven, traditional 'West of England' cloth for the rear. A current Silver Seraph – we felt – was disappointing in its interior quality. Also in the showroom, and for sale, an aeroplane. A Supermarine Spitfire, fully restored and effervescent in its silver paint in the sunshine.

Lessons learned: cars appear as 'great works of art'. Rolls-Royces should be manufactured in the same environs as the workshop – a 'Wow' experience to see! As with the Spitfire – a sense of nostalgia for the craftsmanship of bygone years.

SATURDAY, 20 MARCH 1999

To Cornwall to see the Pendennis Shipyard. The joint managing directors are Dutch and English, with a general manager who is a Breton. They explain the work done at the yard as we walk around looking at the ships in production. A new Maxi 100, a new Wally 107 – mostly constructed of carbon fibre. An old Dutch boat in for a refit and looking like something out of a pirate film. Their facilities are awesome. The yard uses local craftsmen and skills wherever possible and the owners praise the adaptability of the people they use. Under lowering skies and with a fierce wind, we go to another side of the dock to see Rebecca, a 120ft long sailing yacht built for an American client. The attention to detail on Rebecca and the quality of materials used is stunning. We can photograph on deck but not inside as the owner has already installed some personal effects. Rebecca will leave for sea trials in a few days.

Things to remember: the rubber caulking and the rigging. The incredible mixture of high-tech and traditional materials. Impressive craftsmanship everywhere and incredible work ethic behind this craftsmanship. Stunning stainless steel details.

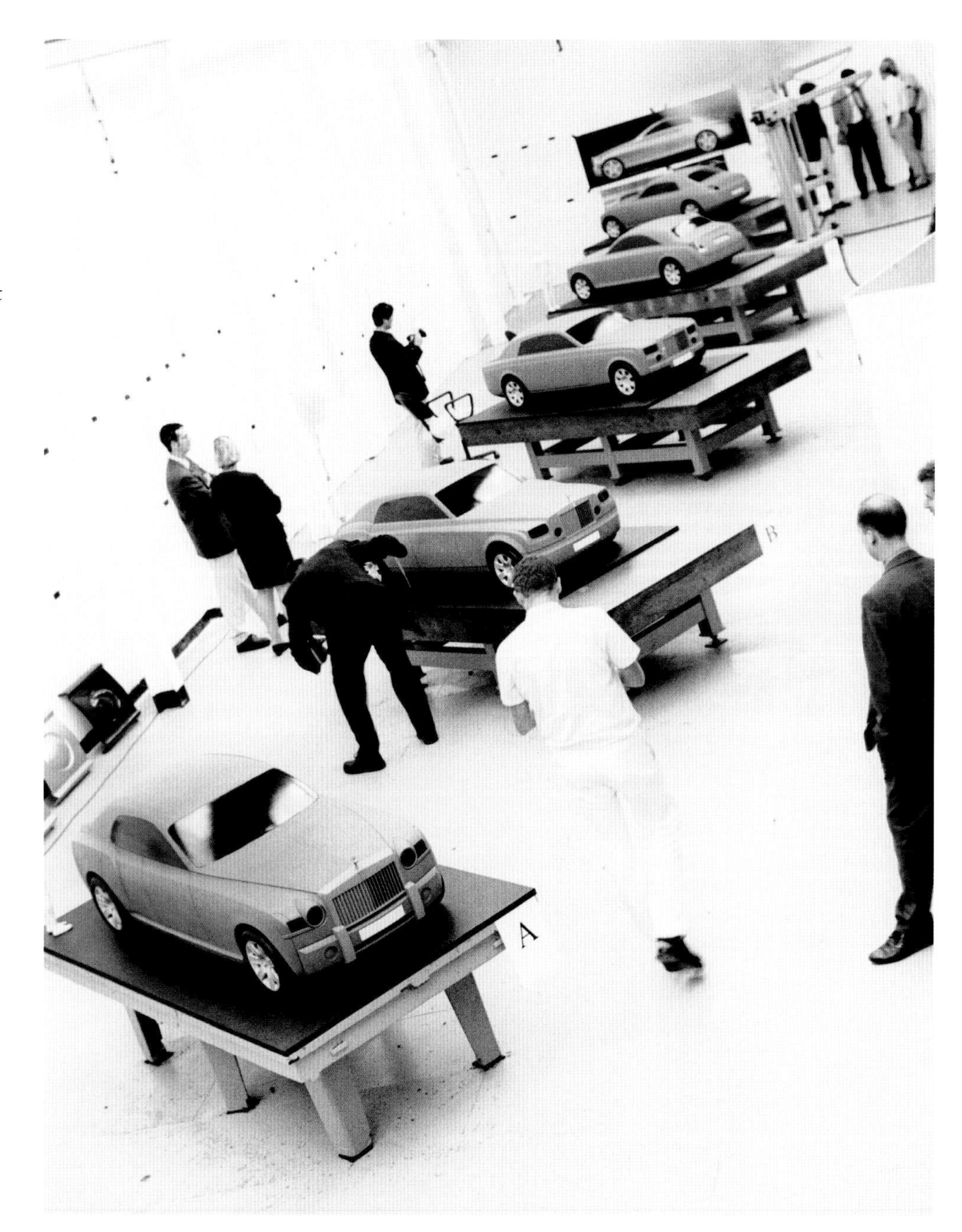

Five of the final concept clay models awaiting judgement.

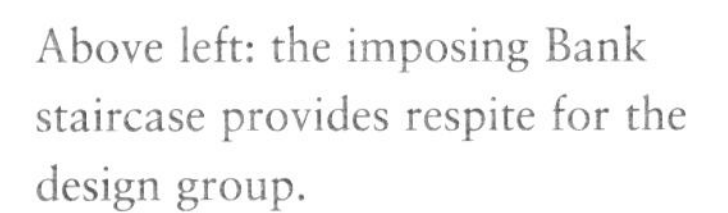

Above left: the imposing Bank staircase provides respite for the design group.

Above right: seating styling proposal awaits consideration by the styling team.

SUNDAY, 21 MARCH 1999

A shaky start on Sunday morning. Up the wooden steps to the deck of Iona. She is 22 metres tall above the waterline and there is a large gap between the steps and her deck, which one of our team members does not appreciate! We tiptoe past the Captain's cabin and begin our visit in the engine room. Two 956bhp Caterpillars, all painted sparkling white and suspended on an air bed. A workbench, innumerable dials and flashing lights. We visit the cockpit, full of black leather seats and couch, black suede walls and black carbon fibre instrument panels. Then on to the deck – Jacuzzi, barbecue and helipad. Down below, elegantly curved staircase to the main deck. Cinema and saloon, guest cabins, owner's state room. All with much marble veined with gold. Family photographs everywhere give a comfortable feeling.

Lessons learned: quality of individual craftsmanship – best in the world; the advantages of dealing directly with your customers.

Styling buck (above) and coloured sketches (right) greatly assisted the decision makers in the evolution of the car.

Part 2

THE ROLLS-ROYCE PHANTOM IN DETAIL

5 INNOVATIVE SPACEFRAME CONSTRUCTION

For any future occupants in a Phantom, it will be a comfort to know that the spaceframe structure is twice as rigid as that of typical luxury saloons

Opposite: a computer-generated Phantom spaceframe awaits 'destruction' at the press of a few buttons in a series of virtual crash tests.

If there is one criterion that has allowed the Phantom to become a reality, then it is the car's spaceframe construction. This type of structural element in car manufacturing is a well established process, but is only now becoming widely applied to production road cars.

A research programme for which Dr. Michael Howard of Bath University was a member, entitled 'Three Day Car' categorises the differences between the three main structural elements in passenger vehicle construction today.

Chassis

"The chassis was the most common type of structure used on the earliest cars of the 1900s. Still used on trucks, 'London'-type purpose-built taxis, and some off-road vehicles, it provides a separate structural platform on to which is mounted a body. Two steel beams or box sections run down the entire length of the vehicle and are joined together by crossmembers, providing strength and rigidity, and giving a low centre of gravity. The construction method of separate chassis and body is favoured by manufacturers for comparatively low-volume, economical vehicle manufacture. Notable long-running examples in the UK have been the Land Rover Defender and Discovery series. An important derivative is the ladder chassis, commonly used in performance cars, combining a slim-line chassis with additional stiffening cross-members for a rigid, lightweight design."

Monocoque

"The monocoque is currently the standard structure for most cars made around the world in high volumes – that is, of 100,000-plus per annum. Constructed from pressed sheet steel, it combines the function of both chassis and body in a three-dimensional structure. In its purest sense, the term monocoque is applied to a structure which relies entirely on its outer skin for strength. A semi-monocoque has stiffening members and transverse frames supporting the skin or outer body panels, and this is the accurate term to use when describing the structure of most cars. While some panels are detachable, such as the doors, bonnet and front wings, the remainder of the outside surface plays a key part in the structural integrity of the vehicle. With the exception of the Jaguar E-type, there are probably no true monocoques on the road today. The monocoque originates from the work of steel pressings pioneer Edward Budd in the 1930s, who developed a separate, structurally independent body that sat on top of the chassis. As chassis and body began to develop as one unit, the increasing popularity of the design meant the economies of scale required could only be

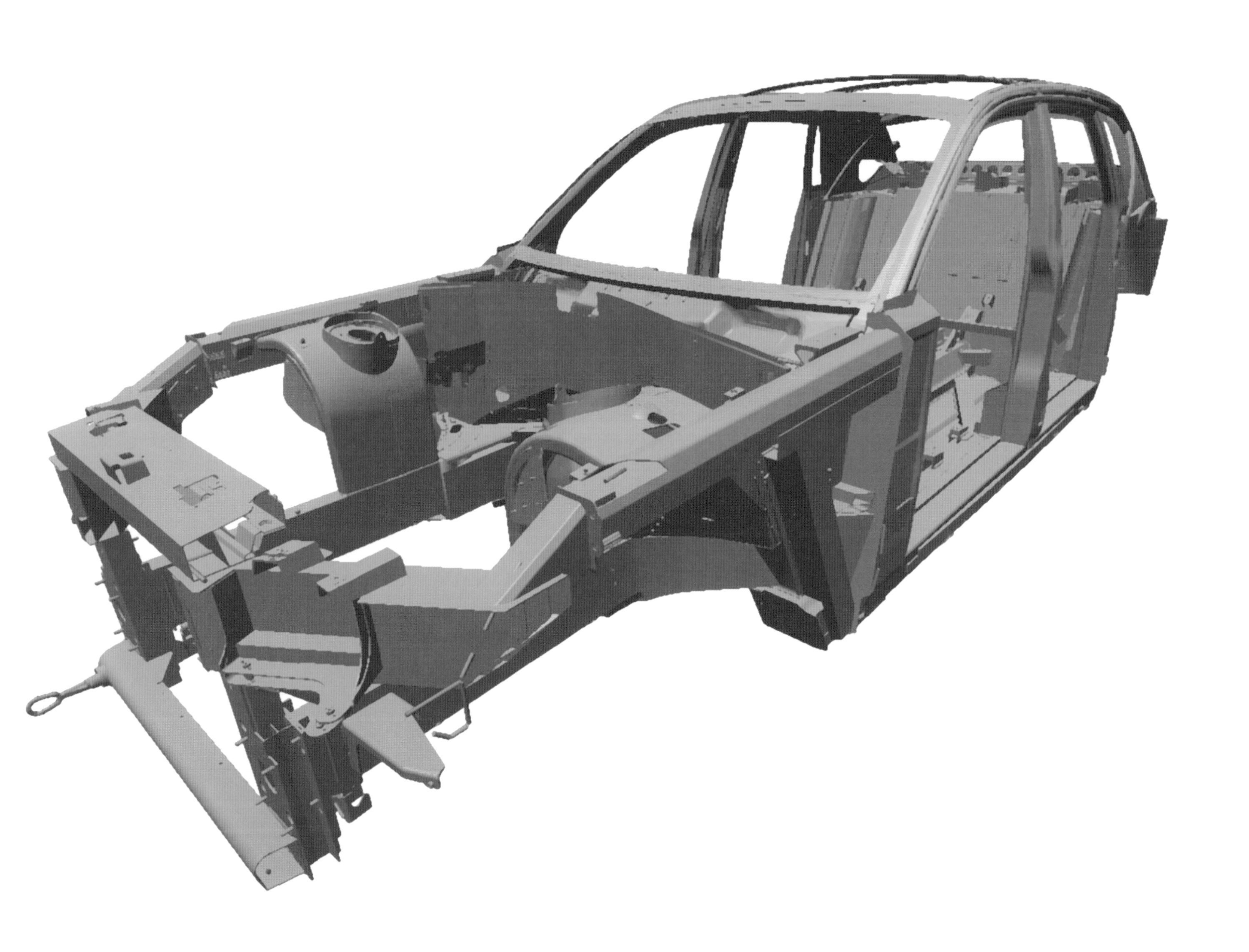

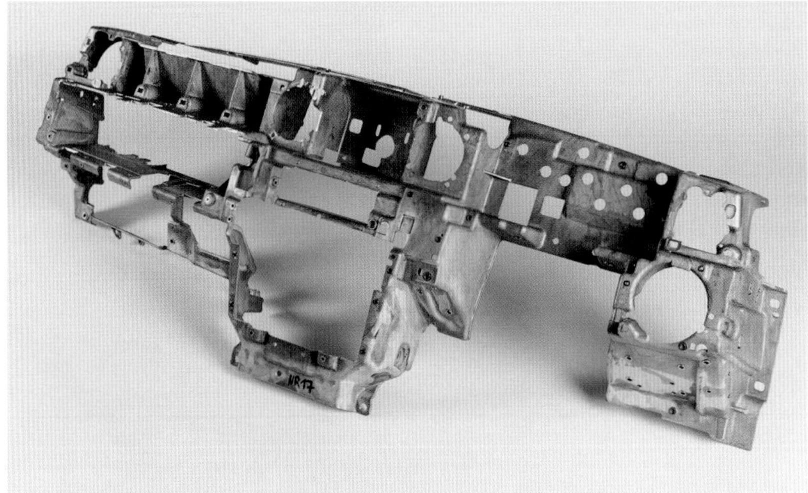

Left: a sectioned spaceframe showing the massive form that imparts so much strength and torsional rigidity.

Right: the 'one-piece' instrument panel carrier cast from magnesium alloy, with its machined faces ready for component attachments.

achieved through the standardisation of parts, and the high volume production of common steel pressings. The success of this 'Buddist Paradigm' led to it becoming almost universal among volume car producers by the 1960s."

Spaceframe

"Originally developed for performance cars such as the Maserati 'Birdcage' sports-racing cars in the early 1960s, spaceframes resembled a 'cage' of welded tubes on to which a non-structural bodyshell was attached. The spaceframe, unlike the monocoque, relied on an internal tubular frame to provide the entire load-bearing qualities of the vehicle. Colin Chapman with his Lotus 8 in 1955 developed an almost perfect lightweight spaceframe. However, in optimising the frame, access to areas such as the engine compartment became severely restricted.

"On current models, outside panels assist only in the crashworthiness of the structure, with the possible exception of the roof panel, which provides some lateral stiffness. Current spaceframes can be constructed from either aluminium or steel extrusions and can readily take advantage of technology like composite panels and high-strength adhesive bonding. Major savings can be achieved of around 30 to 40 per cent in the frame weight.

"Extrusions are an important feature of the spaceframe as they represent a departure from the reliance of conventional manufacture on pressed sheet steel as a means of achieving body stiffness and strength. The total tooling costs associated with either aluminium or steel extrusions in vehicle production are around half that of pressings. A spaceframe is more labour-intensive than a welded-steel monocoque because a greater number of parts are required in constructing the body."

Dr. Michael Howard adds that few automotive body structures represent a pure manifestation of a finite engineering principle – that is, an absolutely pure monocoque or spaceframe is a rarity.

"Similarly, the term 'spaceframe' seems to have been adopted by the automotive press to describe structures which more accurately should be described as hybrids or 'semi-structures'." But the spaceframe term is absolutely correct for the Phantom. It consists of some 200 extruded profiles and over 300 sheet parts. Some 500 feet of welds are executed by hand in approximately 2,000 locations on the completed frame. After assembly, the spaceframe is placed into a custom-built jig where critical fixing points and surfaces are machined with computer-controlled equipment. In this way, all assembly tolerances are accurate to plus or minus 0.5mm, along the length of the car, for the location of major items such as doors, engine and suspension mounting points. The spaceframe is the car's structure so all the outer skin panels and doors, front wings, bonnet and boot lid are mounted to it using rivets and fasteners.

The strength of the completed spaceframe of the Phantom is well able to withstand the most stringent crash-testing. The event that would be most feared by crash test dummies, assuming they had human brains,

A prototype spaceframe on test. Note the front section where the Rolls-Royce radiator and grille would be attached.

is the 'deformable barrier 40mph impact with 40 per cent frontal overlap' test. Both in computer simulations and in real-life crash-testing, however, the Phantom copes more than adequately with this, there being almost no intrusion into the passenger cabin at toe level. Forces are dissipated throughout the structure, illustrated by the energy-absorbing ripples that would be seen along the roof skin in such an unfortunate impact.

Dr. Tim Leverton, the project's chief engineer, joined the Bank design team four weeks after its inauguration. He had been a sponsored student at British Leyland in 1977, staying with the descendants of the company throughout the 1980s and 1990s. His last job before joining Project Rolls-Royce was working on the concept styling programme for the new Range Rover. Leverton is proud of the fact that the Phantom has the largest production spaceframe for a passenger car in the world. To achieve this, he and his team had to overcome difficulties caused by welding such large areas without distortion.

"You couldn't just weld along a row," he says. "You had to work out where stresses would be caused and use careful positioning of components to relieve those stresses as much as possible."

Despite the intentional and successful separation of Project Rolls-Royce from its German parent, Ian Cameron is quick to give unconditional praise to the Dingolfing body manufacturing plant, BMW's centre of competence for spaceframe technology. "There is an aluminium expertise that you cannot match anywhere else. It happens to be in the [BMW] group and I don't think we should be coy about declaring that."

Although not strictly part of the spaceframe, the instrument panel carrier is worthy of mention here. Made of a single piece of magnesium alloy, this massive unit has a multitude of machined surfaces to take mounting points for all the items attached to the facia. Strength was therefore added to the car's structure by using an ultra-lightweight piece of engineering and, being a single item, the possibility of squeaks and rattles would be reduced to very nearly zero.

The initial development of a spaceframe is easier and quicker than that of a monocoque unit with its designated floorpan. Tooling costs are greatly reduced and, in the long term, it is easier to alter the dimensions of the spaceframe. The intrinsic strength of the spaceframe unit allows aluminium to be used in place of steel with an average weight saving of some 40 per cent.

This, of course, is one of the main reasons the Phantom is capable of such rapid acceleration and braking performance. And, as such, is among the most important 'inner secrets' of the reborn Rolls-Royce.

A completed spaceframe, fully panelled, is examined for imperfections at the Dingolfing body plant, BMW's centre of competence for spaceframe technology.

6 POWER IN THE BEST ROLLS-ROYCE TRADITION

Waftability: Power without apparent effort – THE AUTOCAR, 1906

Opposite: meticulous assembly ensures trouble-free use between recommended services.

Emerge from the tunnel as you grind through the traffic entering London's Heathrow airport and you will see a statue of two early aviators, Captain John Alcock and Lieutenant Arthur Brown who, in 1919, made the first non-stop transatlantic flight. Their Vickers Vimy was powered by two Rolls-Royce Eagle engines. In the mid 1990s, a re-creation of the Vimy aircraft was privately built. It was to be as close to the original as possible, except that modern engines would be used to propel it for safety reasons. The power units chosen were BMW V12 car engines, suitably modified for aviation use. Who would have thought that such a portent of engineering substitution would also prove so appropriate in the rebirth of the Rolls-Royce motor car?

As already mentioned, the Silver Seraph was the first Rolls-Royce to be powered by BMW; indeed, it was the first to have an engine that was not manufactured by Rolls-Royce. It was not a complete success in that configuration as it lacked torque low down in the rev range. Capable of performing well if the throttle was used with enthusiasm, the car was not deemed to have the crucial 'waftability' factor.

To develop a completely new engine for a low-volume production car like the Phantom is economically prohibitive. Under almost 20 years of ownership by Vickers, Rolls-Royce had become well aware that a replacement unit was overdue for the brilliant but ageing 6.75 litre V8. This had been designed under the watchful eye of technical director Harry Grylls in the 1950s, but was coming to the end of its useful life, both in terms of power and its ability to comply with the ever-tightening noose of emission control demands. Often wrongly referred to as 'an American engine built under licence', it was in fact designed entirely by Rolls-Royce. Only the concept of a pushrod V8 configured engine was American.

By the end of 2002, BMW had developed a new V12 engine for its 7 Series that was capable of being adapted to supply motive power in true Rolls-Royce fashion. It is unlikely BMW could have made a clear financial case for buying Rolls-Royce without having this excellent basis for RR01's engine ready to develop. Project Rolls-Royce and BMW engineers worked in parallel on a dedicated production line at BMW's Munich engine facility. Incidentally, Adolf Fischer, the engineer most closely associated with the project, had also been a mainstay for those re-created Vickers Vimy engines, as well as the bespoke power plant developed for the McLaren F1.

Working so closely with BMW meant the Project Rolls-Royce team could have as much technical back-up as they required, while never compromising their essential autonomy for the development of the RR01 engine. Karl Baumer and Dr. Tim Leverton oversaw the

ENGINE OIL

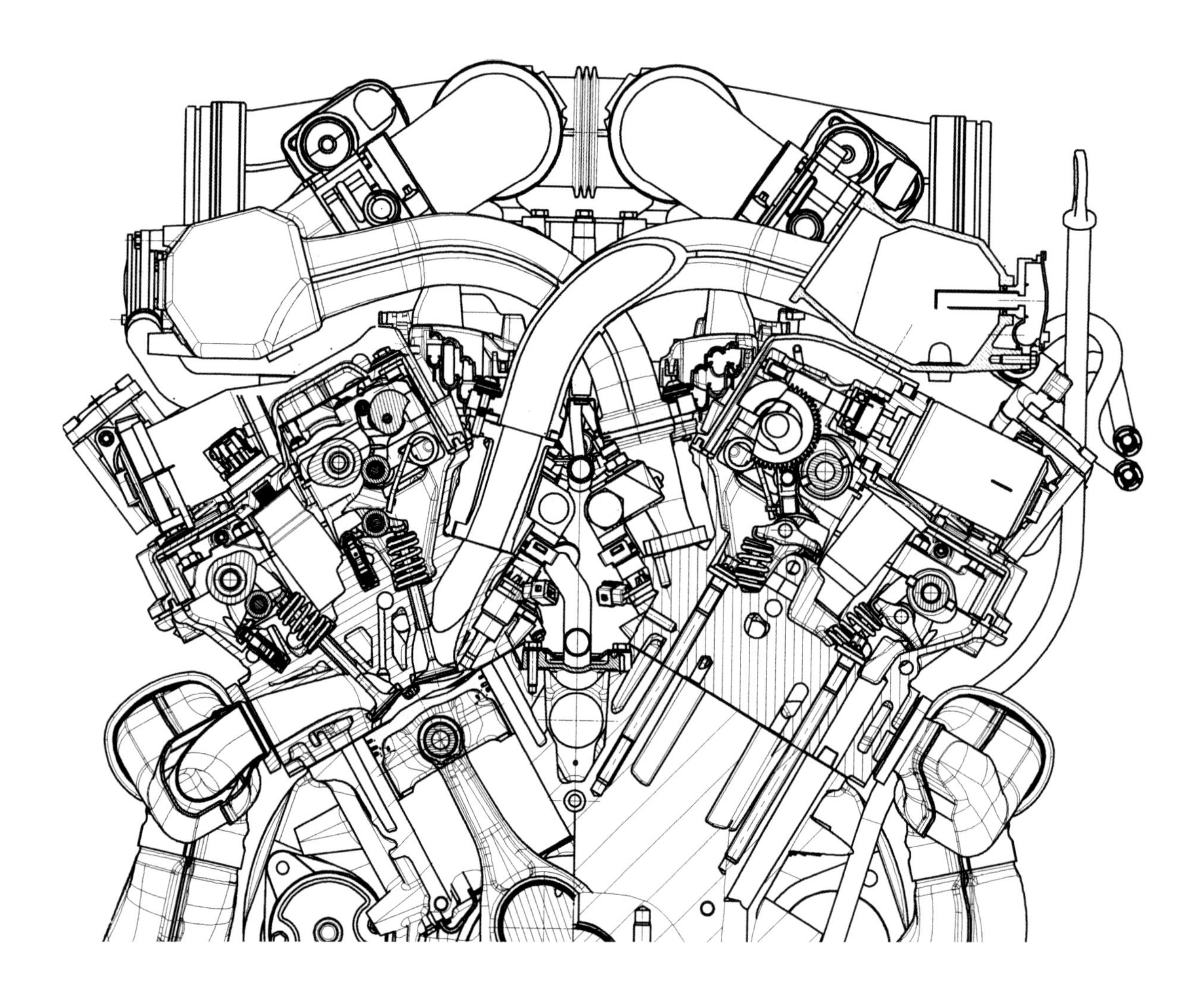

Above: engineering or artistry? The Phantom's V12 engine offers 6.75 litres of gentle 'waftability' power.

Opposite: direct fuel-injection and long intake pipes permit the Phantom's required low-down torque.

engineers who adapted the cylinder heads and inlet manifolds that would make this possible. The normally-aspirated, all-alloy 60 degree V12 had its bore and stroke increased to 92x84.6mm, which produced the traditional Rolls-Royce capacity of 6.75 litres. Work was underway to achieve the low-speed torque – key to attaining the elusive quality of 'waftability'.

Thus, the torque curve is flat in character. At 1000rpm, the engine has 15 per cent more torque available than the peak torque of the Silver Seraph at 4000rpm. But why was this so desirable? Tim Leverton explains: "The flatness of this curve is important through the engine speed range of 1000-3000rpm, which is the typical engine speed range for normal city driving. Every time the driver depresses the throttle pedal, the car picks up smoothly and without hesitation. This is the essential quality of waftability. By contrast, with a turbocharged engine, the driver has to wait until the engine has reached approximately 2000rpm before rocket propulsion kicks in. The absence of sufficient torque from rest demands a wider throttle opening to elicit a response, leading to the risk that manoeuvres through busy traffic entail the engine continually moving up and down a much steeper torque curve. Potential for wheelspin at 80mph perhaps, but not waftability."

Peter Baines, general secretary of the Rolls-Royce Enthusiasts' Club, supplied the team with the torque figures for the Phantom III of the late 1930s. Leverton continues: "We were a little surprised to see how much torque the Phantom III had. It equates to an acceleration time of 6.3 seconds for 25-40mph. Incidentally, the Phantom completes the same manoeuvre in 2.2 seconds."

The engine's everyday performance and the needs of emission control legislation meant adopting a unique petrol injection system. Thus, a single high-pressure jet for each cylinder now supplies a precisely measured

ROLLS-ROYCE

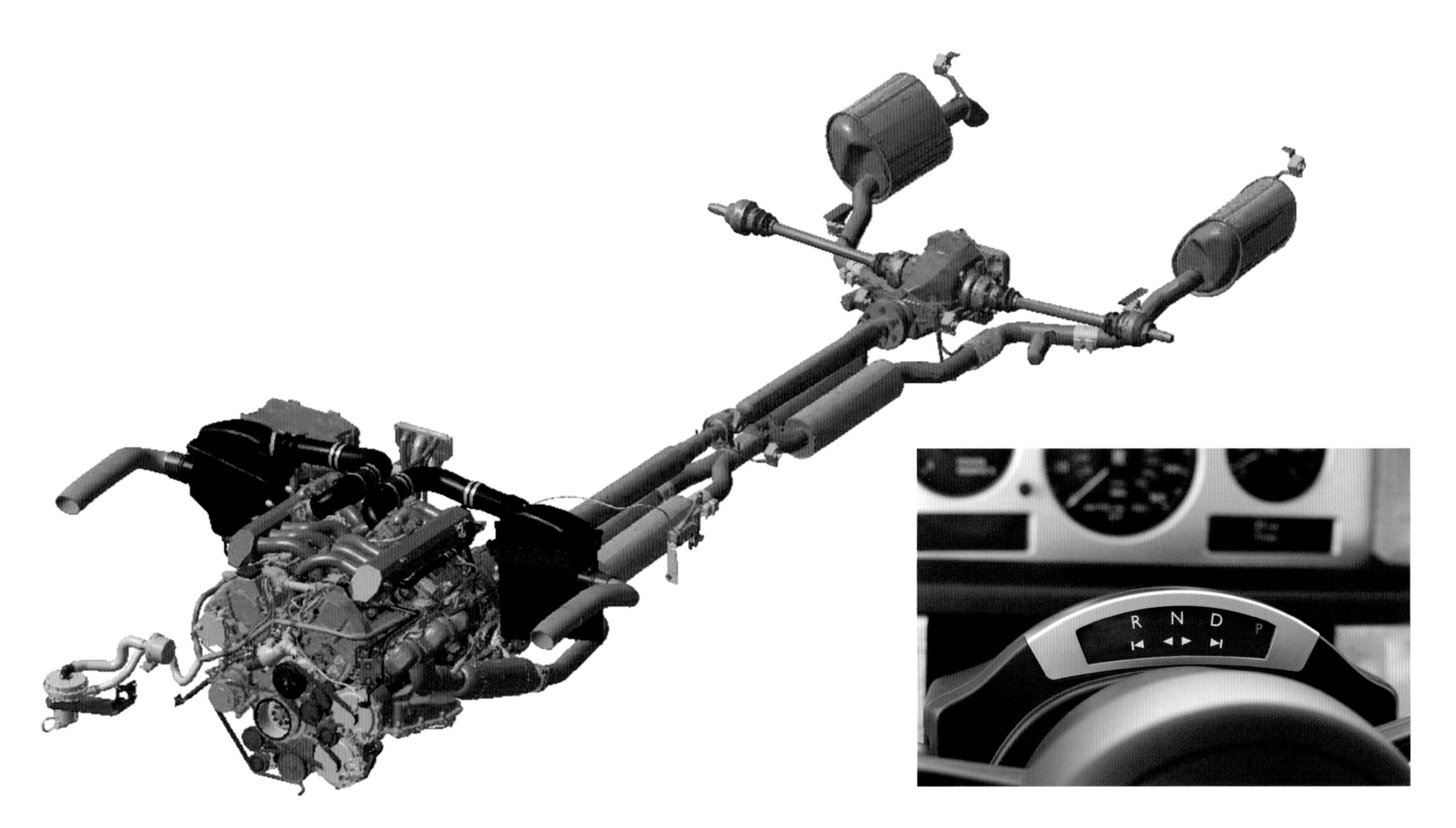

Above left: computer colour-coded image shows the Phantom's entire powertrain for easy identification of component parts.

Above right: the gear selector indicator is a time-honoured Rolls-Royce detail which has now been simplified for the Phantom's 'Authority Concept'.

amount of fuel directly into each combustion chamber. This evaporating spray of fuel has a cooling effect, which allows a raised compression ratio of 11:1. In turn, this produces a higher thermal efficiency, which gives greater power and torque.

A system of variable camshaft timing of up to 60 per cent combined with a variable valve lift mechanism was the next consideration. Control of the 48 valves regulates the air intake precisely throughout the rev range, maximising the engine's efficiency. This not only reduces fuel consumption but also aids the desired torque curve. The fuel efficiency of this unit allied to the relatively low weight of the Phantom gives a combined fuel consumption of 17.8mpg, with 20mpg easily attainable at constant cruising speeds. The fuel tank can hold 22 gallons.

Traditionally, Rolls-Royce declared the brake horsepower figure as simply 'adequate'. In the case of the Phantom, this coyness is replaced by the proud statement that 453bhp has been achieved. Tim Leverton was asked how much power was in reserve when cruising at the British legal speed limit of 70mph. "Oh," he replied, casually, "about 93 per cent!"

Once the carefully monitored and controlled fuel air mixture has done its job, it is expelled from the engine by means of a dual stainless steel exhaust system. Six silencers or 'resonators' expand and cool the spent gas on its way out to the atmosphere. At any speed, the resulting exhaust noise can only be called a gentle purr. When an owner wishes to make an especially quiet arrival or departure, a 'whisper valve' in the rear resonators closes to allow near silent movement – subject, of course, to the depth of gravel beneath the tyres!

Power reaches the rear wheels via a six-speed Model 6HP32 automatic gearbox from transmission experts ZF. It is connected to the gear selector electronically, 'shift-by-wire' being the automotive industry shorthand for this. There is a wide spread of ratios that give crisp acceleration – the Phantom speeds to 60mph in just 5.7 seconds – and relaxed high speed cruising; upward shifts occur early, and downward ones late. Although there is an emergency kickdown on the throttle pedal, the characteristically massive torque means a higher gear remains for longer periods than with other cars. Normal starts from rest are in second gear, unless a rapid departure is sensed, in which case first is selected. There is also a 'low' button on the steering wheel, which engages a special 'Low

The engine may be virtually silent in the Phantom but, when testing it this close, 453bhp demands some ear protection!

Programme' intended for use in mountainous terrain. The gearbox controller has adaptive control software which monitors and learns the style of the driver, altering the gear selection appropriately.

So what of real-life performance for the Phantom? Tony Gott, long-time Rolls-Royce man and now chairman and chief executive officer of the new company, says: "In Europe, the car is limited to 150mph. But it's not about who can accelerate faster or who has the highest top speed. What's the point – should every car be a land speed record holder? No. The Phantom delivers all the performance you will need in the real world."

7 SUSPENSION TO COSSET PASSENGERS AND DELIGHT DRIVERS

Creating a Rolls-Royce is not about achieving a single superlative but rather about finding an optimum balance of attributes. Excellence is in the detail often unseen to the casual observer

– TONY GOTT, CHAIRMAN, ROLLS-ROYCE MOTOR CARS

Opposite: as the Phantom gathers speed, the linked R-R emblem in the wheel centres remains upright, visually enhancing waftability.

For any vehicle to make the most of its suspension system, it needs as rigid a chassis/body structure as can be achieved. It must be sensitive over the complete range of loads, speeds and surfaces.

The Phantom, with its uniquely designed spaceframe structure, comes close to being the perfect platform to which the suspension engineers can attach their hardware. The long wheelbase intrinsic to the Phantom philosophy promotes a smooth ride and the positioning and composition of the Rolls-Royce's components equalises the weight distribution, even to the point of using steel for the boot lid instead of lightweight aluminium, to get the balance just right.

Dr. Tim Leverton was adamant the suspension would be as nearly perfect as possible across the entire anticipated performance range. For the front, a double-wishbone arrangement was specified, with a tension link and lower control arm. Highly controlled camber and track changes over the whole range of movement were employed, including anti-dive characteristics under hard braking. There is even a hydraulic mount in the front suspension to damp out any vibration that may otherwise be transmitted to the steering wheel. The suspension is mounted on a tubular steel subframe for precise geometry, reduced noise and crash protection enhancement. The subframe itself is rigidly attached to the body at six points.

On the rear of the car, the multi-link suspension is designed for superlative ride comfort, as well as resisting the rise of the rear under braking, and dive during acceleration. Unlike the steel front subframe, the rear frame is manufactured from 5mm thick hydroformed aluminium extrusions, and it uses large bushes to isolate chassis-borne driveline noise and vibration from the rest of the car. For both front and rear, anti-roll bars are mounted to the subframes with roller bearings for low friction and low noise. The suspension links are also in aluminium. The cast lower arms sit parallel to the road in the normal position and have an aerodynamic effect in smoothing the flow of air that exits from underneath the back of the moving Phantom.

Air springs are used all around for their ability to sustain constant soft spring rates and full travel regardless of load. So sensitive is this system, it can react to a rear seat passenger moving from one side of the car to the other. The air springs can be raised by the driver, up to one inch if conditions (such as rough ground) demand it and, should he or she forget to lower the springs, they will automatically return to the lower position when the car reaches 37mph.

RR01's dampers are electronically controlled. It has minimal damping for straight smooth roads, progressing to higher damping on corners and bumpy surfaces. In this way, both excellent passenger comfort and precise

ROLLS
RR
ROYCE

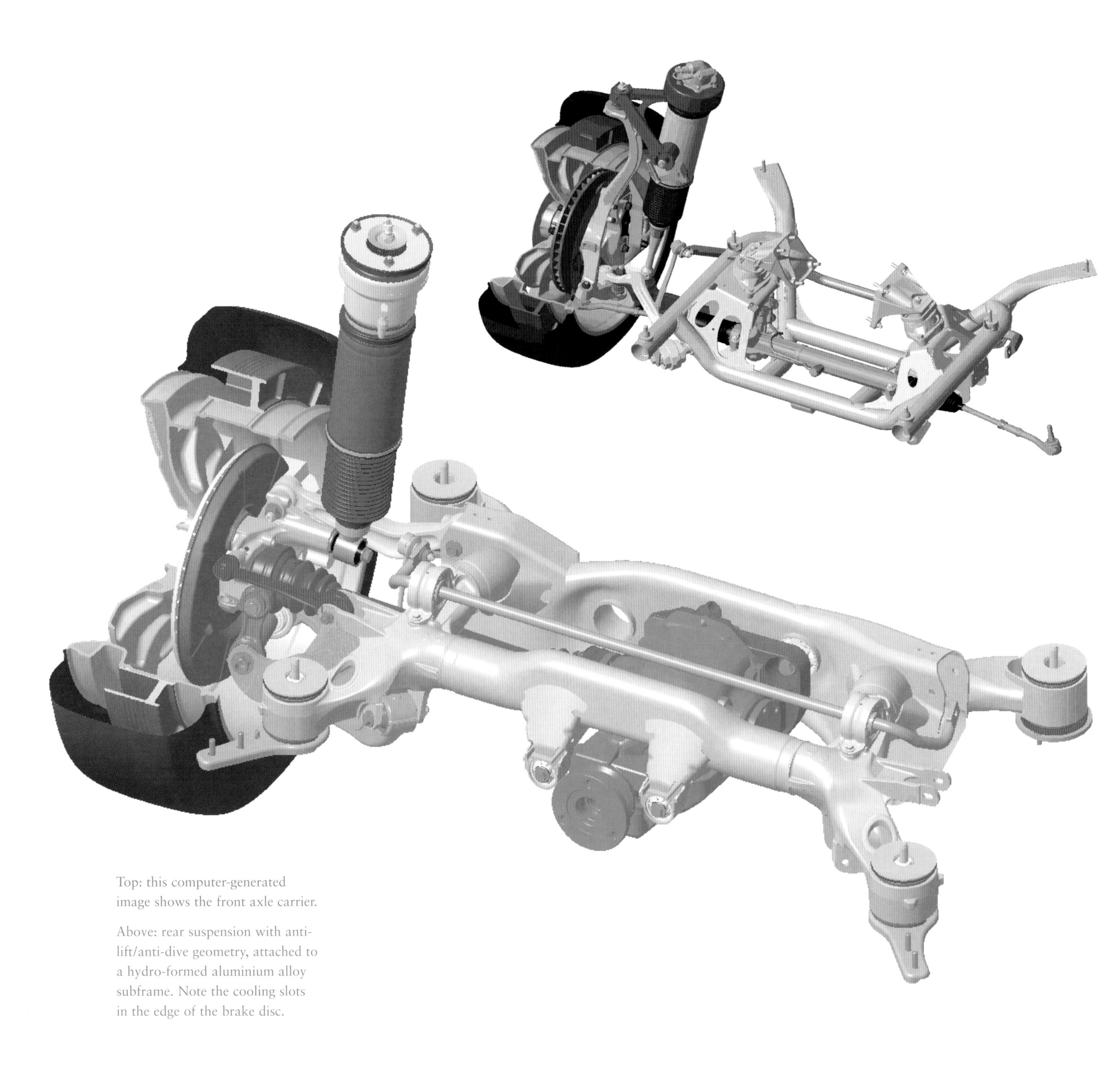

Top: this computer-generated image shows the front axle carrier.

Above: rear suspension with anti-lift/anti-dive geometry, attached to a hydro-formed aluminium alloy subframe. Note the cooling slots in the edge of the brake disc.

Left: with wheel removed, the rear suspension with its anti-lift/anti-dive geometry can be seen, along with the air spring and shock absorber.

Right: the massive Michelin PAX system run-flat tyre surrounds the PAX 265x540A aluminium alloy wheel.

handling can be achieved simultaneously. The system monitors both the way the car is being driven and the prevailing road condition up to 100 times a second, or every 12 inches at 60mph.

One of the hardest tasks for the development engineers was the secondary ride optimisation – which means, in short, how the car rides over short frequency-corrugations. From the very beginning, the designers wanted RR01 to have large wheels, although some seasoned hands at the BMW parent company needed time and persuasion to accept that philosophy. Chief designer Ian Cameron was adamant that what he called the "Rolls-Royceness" of the car would be threatened if the marque's traditional wheel size of about one half the car's overall height was not adopted.

The unsprung weight – which means any part of a car not supported by its suspension system, such as wheels, axles and brakes – is set at a hefty 100kg. The non-mechanically minded might ask: so what? But one must consider that, every time a wheel hits a bump or pothole, the hard-worked suspension is obliged to absorb the forces of that mass as it moves up or down. On top of which, the steering, acceleration and braking must never be compromised. After much reworking, the unsprung mass was reduced to 90kg, a less cumbersome weight for the suspension components to handle.

The suspension of the test cars showed acceptable results on special test tracks in Munich but, when the cars were driven around typical English country roads, more needed to be done. The combination of tight corners, often S-bends requiring rapid changes in direction, and poor road surfaces meant a major suspension revision, just when everything had looked perfect. Head of Engineering Karl Baumer also knew that one of the Phantom's core strengths was causing the problem – its relative lightness compared to the weight of the wheels. The answer was to rework the mass of the wheel and brake, and alter the spring and shock absorber settings. Immediately the problem was solved.

Tim Leverton puts the problem into layman's terms: "If you drive any Rolls-Royce from the last 20 years or so, then you have an excellent primary ride, or 'low-frequency' ride [the way the suspension behaves as the car is being driven in a straight line] which is a typical Rolls-Royce feature. In terms of effortless driving, it quickly turns into a problem when you want to drive the car around a corner, rolling and generally feeling uncomfortable.

"I always had in mind that the Phantom would be pleasant to drive at all times," he adds. "It would not wallow, it would not be harsh – it would float above all the imperfections the road could offer. Not in the sense of it being a sports car, but a very easy car to drive, giving you a feeling of complete control at all times."

8 THE 'LIMBS' OF THE PHANTOM: STEERING, WHEELS AND BRAKES

Accept nothing nearly right or good enough – SIR HENRY ROYCE

Opposite: the underside of the Phantom, showing the balanced exhaust system.

The driver's seat of the Phantom is a great place to find oneself. All the benefits of the car's 'Authority Concept' make it so, and one is finally in command of the machine with all the performance and mechanical accuracy it has to offer via its beautifully weighted controls.

Even the steering wheel adds to the Rolls-Royce experience, having a large-diameter rim that is also quite thin in the best tradition of the marque, and by comparison with other modern luxury cars. It would have been easy and cost-effective to simply adopt an existing design, but Ian Cameron was sure that a steering wheel for RR01 needed to be custom-designed for the car, and the chosen dimensions should be "very Rolls-Royce". It is not simply a matter of size and shape with steering wheels today, for in this safety-conscious world, governed by stringent regulations, the wheel must house an air bag and conform to many other requirements. For the Phantom, the design also called for the return of the wheel-mounted controls redolent of the Phantom III of the 1930s, and thus to create a uniquely intimate 'bridge' between driver and machine. In this case, if the wheel looked or felt wrong, then the special driving experience that was craved would be compromised. Not surprisingly, this was all very costly to execute to the total satisfaction of international safety legislators and testers.

Tim Leverton was in agreement with the design team that the steering wheel must be directly on the centre line of the driver. It is surprising how many cars today have wheel and driver's seat or pedals slightly, yet uncomfortably, offset from one another. This does not matter on a short trip once one has become used to the irritation, but it is slowly and relentlessly tiring on a long journey.

"It might be thought that a Rolls-Royce is big enough to make this steering wheel position easy to achieve," says Leverton. "But it is more difficult than it appears. When we look at the driving position in plan view, the top section of the steering column is installed directly on the centre line of the driver. Then each joint in the column is used to its maximum to move the steering gear inboard, so it misses the inside face of the front longitudinal structure – effectively, 'angling' the column in towards the middle of the car. The achievement of centre line steering wheel positioning was quite critical; ultimately, the only limitations put on us were the size of the road wheels and the maintenance of a realistic turning circle."

One cannot avoid mention of suspension settings when writing of a car's steering because, as far as the driver is concerned, the one has a direct effect on the other. For a car to steer with impeccable manners at slow and medium speeds, it will be compromised, albeit slightly, at high speeds, and vice versa. Leverton felt that,

The six-speed ZF 6HP32 gearbox, operated by 'shift-by-wire' technology, will select top gear quickly.

with RR01's initial settings, the speed-sensitive rack and pinion steering was a little too direct at very high speeds (130mph-plus) but this setting did give a good 'feel' at slow and medium speeds.

There was some discussion as to at what speed the steering should feel best, and in the end it was decided to select the slow and medium speeds. The resulting downside to this is that a sudden 'jiggle' at speed could cause a reaction at the road wheels large enough to affect the car's directional stability, even if only marginally.

Leverton remembers: "At the end of May 2002, we drove the car around central London for two days. The whole episode had started in the multi-storey car park at Heathrow Airport's Terminal 1 – up and down, round and round, just to make sure we could! This caused a lot of amusement.

Driving back from London to Chichester along the winding roads of Surrey and Sussex, we knew we had made the right choice. What we had done was trade-off the potential for unimpeachable high-speed stability for more authoritative control at normal speeds – everyday driving speeds."

So the Phantom driver experiences relatively direct steering; a ride when driving dead straight that is just floating but never loose, and excellent body control in corners. This also means that, when driving in a more spirited fashion, the driver will not lose any control over the car: it will feel effortless and he or she will maintain complete mastery over the machine.

Rolls-Royce decided to ignore the fashionable trend for low-profile tyres adorning large-diameter road wheels. This is quite acceptable for sports cars and high-performance versions of large saloons where hard-charging driving characteristics are an essential tenet of the package, but low-profile tyres generally compromise ride quality. The Phantom was planned to sit on large

Chief designer Ian Cameron agrees the fine detail of the steering wheel, while a colleague looks on.

wheels with a lot of rubber underneath them – in fact, as it turned out, the largest wheels now fitted on a production passenger car.

As mentioned previously, the one problem that proved the most difficult for the Rolls-Royce engineers to solve was that of the large road wheels, which the speed-sensitive power steering, with its 3.3 turns from lock to lock, needed to control. Especially designed for the Phantom, the Michelin PAX 265x540A aluminium wheels are shod with Michelin PAX 265x790 R540A 111W radial tyres. These tyres have a 'run-flat' capability after a puncture of at least 100 miles at 50mph, and there is also a tyre pressure alert system on the dashboard. Interestingly, they also obviate the need to carry a spare wheel, tyre or jack, thereby reducing weight and increasing luggage space.

This exclusive Michelin PAX system features a specific tyre bead and wheel rim cross-section with an internal support ring that stops the tyre becoming completely flat when deflated. So good is it at controlling the directional stability of the Phantom after a blowout that the tyre pressure alert becomes a necessary warning rather than an electronic gimmick, to let the driver know he has sustained a puncture, to moderate his speed, and find a suitable place within the next 100 miles, such as the nearest Rolls-Royce dealership, for a tyre change.

The wheels themselves are another fine example of the designers' wishes to create a modern interpretation of a classic Rolls-Royce theme. Nine 'spokes' support the rim and the wheel centres have a body colour-coded or chrome-finished surround to a nave plate bearing the linked R-R logo. These nave plates are weighted and can rotate independently of the wheels so, while the wheel is turning, the linked R-R remains upright and readable at all times. A true enhancement of 'waftability' to the onlooker.

Axle and hub assembly ready for fitting to driveline jig, prior to precisely locating on the Phantom's subframe.

Above: a cutaway view of the Michelin PAX run-flat tyre – when flat the tyre offers the lifeline of driving at least 100 miles at 50mph.

Right: rarely seen, the symmetry of the Phantom's underside sustains the engineer's adage that 'if it looks right, it is right'.

The Phantom features four very large disc brakes, 374x36mm at the front and 370x24mm at the rear. These brakes are controlled by a four-channel anti-lock braking system (ABS), which also facilitate a range of dynamic sensor-control systems: Cornering Brake Control (CBC) helps keep the car on its intended course during cornering manoeuvres; Dynamic Brake Control (DBC) senses when full-on emergency braking is called for; anti-slip Dynamic Traction Control (DTC) counters wheelspin on slippery surfaces; and Dynamic Stability Control (DSC) selectively applies individual brakes to reduce the possibility of a skid.

All these system functions greatly enhance the 'Authority Concept' by keeping the driver on-course and helping to minimise human error. However, as always, the Phantom driver remains the car's greatest adjunct to enjoyable but safe driving.

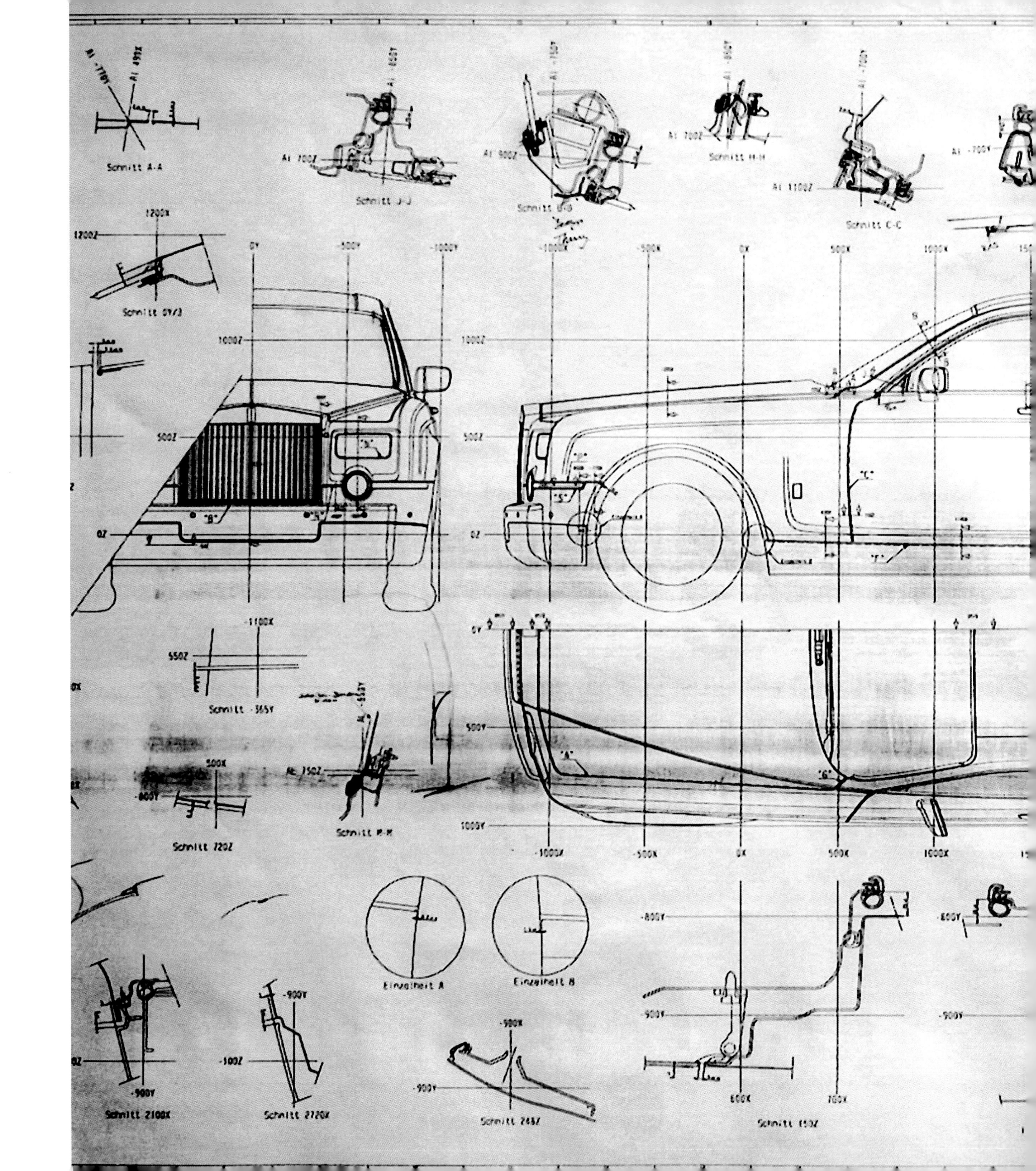

Schnitt A-A
Schnitt J-J
Schnitt B-B
Schnitt H-H
Schnitt C-C
Schnitt 0Y/3
Schnitt -365Y
Schnitt 720Z
Schnitt M-M
Einzelheit A
Einzelheit B
Schnitt 2100X
Schnitt 2720X
Schnitt 248Z
Schnitt 150Z

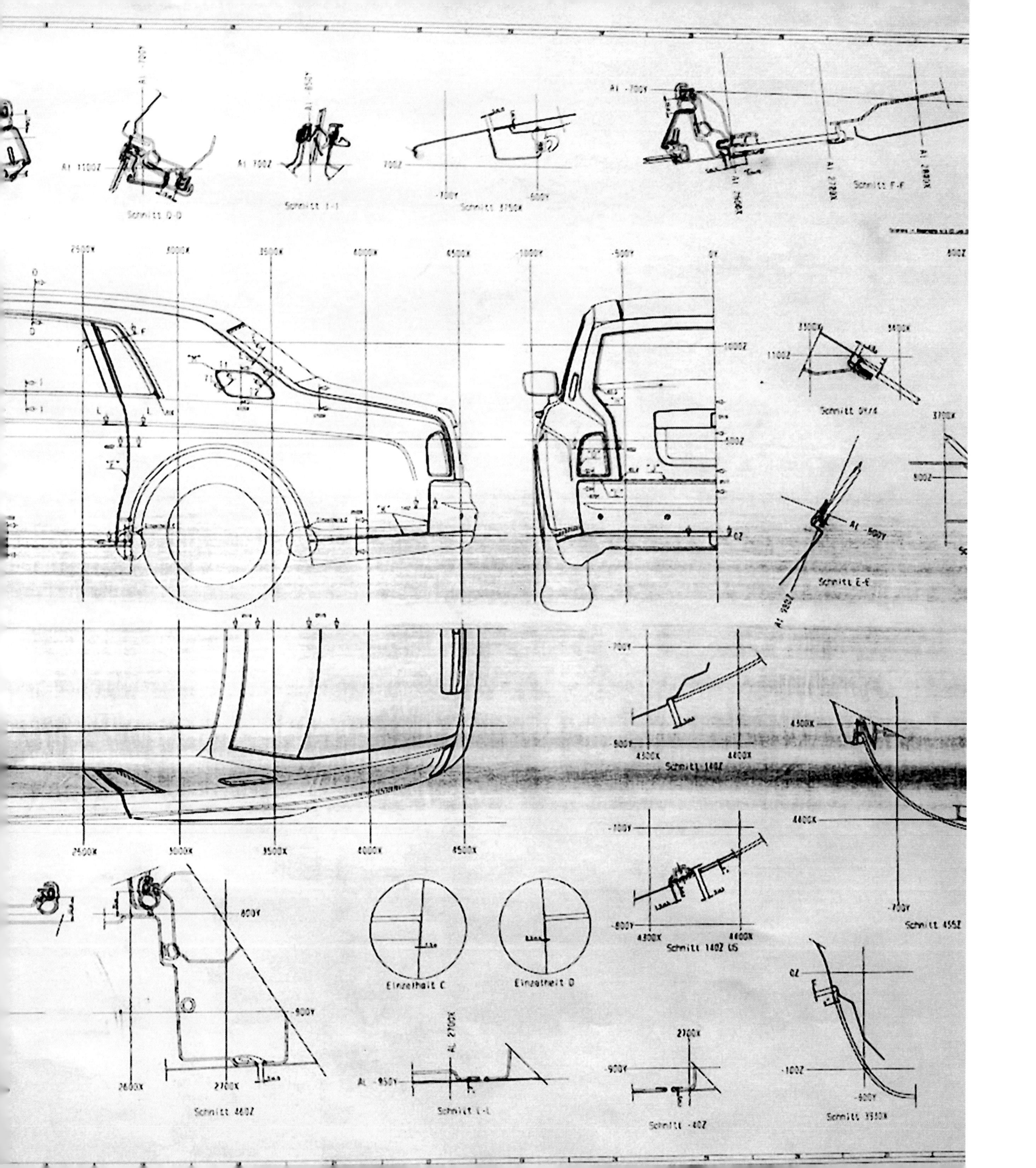
Schnitt D-D
Schnitt I-I
Schnitt 3750X
Schnitt F-F
Schnitt E-E
Schnitt 140Z
Schnitt 140Z US
Schnitt 455Z
Einzelheit C
Einzelheit D
Schnitt 460Z
Schnitt -40Z

9 A TECHNOLOGICAL MARVEL

Any sufficiently advanced technology is indistinguishable from magic

– ARTHUR C CLARKE

Opposite: the 'variable valve lift' mechanism regulates the air intake precisely throughout the rev range; fuel efficiency is maximised and the desired torque curve is easier to achieve.

An engineering principle is one thing; the manner in which it can be realised as a component or system is another. Human knowledge has advanced to the stage where the most complex mechanical systems can be manufactured from eminently suitable materials, custom-designed for the task in hand. Computers are now so powerful and small in size that they can command and monitor virtually any system within a modern automobile. All well and good but as the old saying goes, 'there is no such thing as a free lunch', and the price to be paid by the customer for this particular technological feast is that the car becomes more expensive. There is also a great temptation for manufacturers to supply too much information and too many controls so that the driver becomes confused.

Of course, many technological systems work away quietly behind the scenes. On the Phantom, for instance, the various road wheel and brake monitors reduce the risk of an accident caused by driver error. Even the irritation of roadside wheel-changing has been eliminated by the run-flat Michelin PAX system. In fact, the more sophisticated a car becomes, the more likely that any mishap that occurs will be caused by driver error. The weakest link in the entire car will be the nut behind the wheel!

Only a proportion of the technological systems are related to safety. Reduced fuel consumption and pollution, gear-selection and wiper speeds or the 'soft' shutting of doors are now all the better for being monitored. The Phantom's entertainment system is a fusion of state-of-the-art sound reproduction (optional video for the rear seat occupants) combined with excellent positioning within the car's cabin. The Lexicon Logic7™ audio system has no fewer than 15 metal matrix speakers, which produce the lowest distortion and the most linear performance ever experienced in an automobile. The result of Logic7™ to the human ear is that if, for instance, the passengers are listening to a singer with a backing band, they will hear the vocalist in front of them and the music will be arrayed around the singer, giving a natural 'live' performance.

Air-conditioning is no longer the art of supplying freezing cold air to the knees or necks. The Phantom's system conditions the air – 'climate control', if you will – utilising six separate zones within the car: front and back, left and right, upper and lower. Minimal draughts are felt as the system supplies air through many vents slowly rather than through a few vents quickly. There are 10 metal air vents and numerous concealed outlets throughout the cabin.

This, along with 'all-window' demisting to the infrared radiation-reducing glass, and heated door-mounted mirrors not only bring temperature and humidity-controlled air to the individual occupants, but

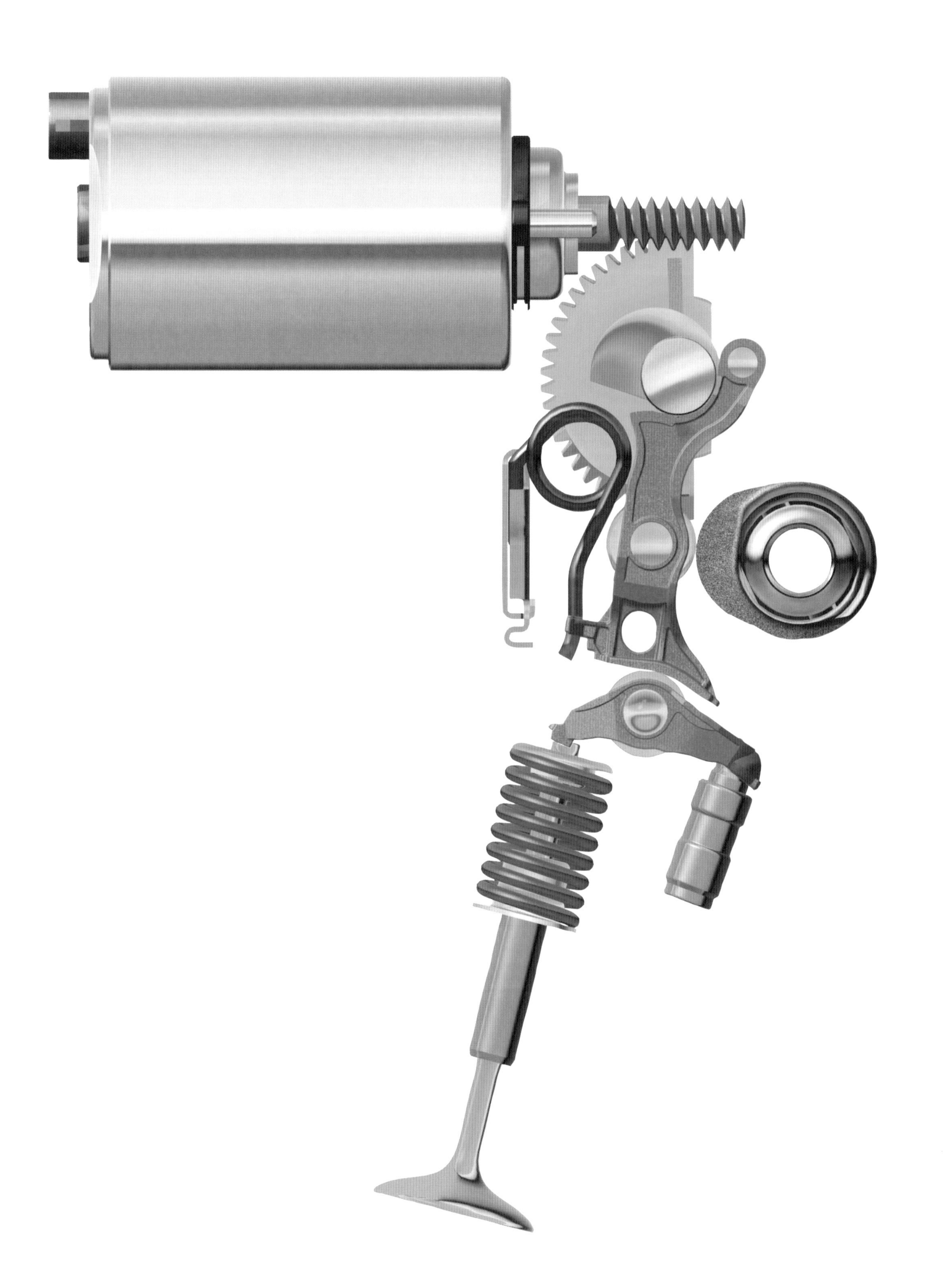

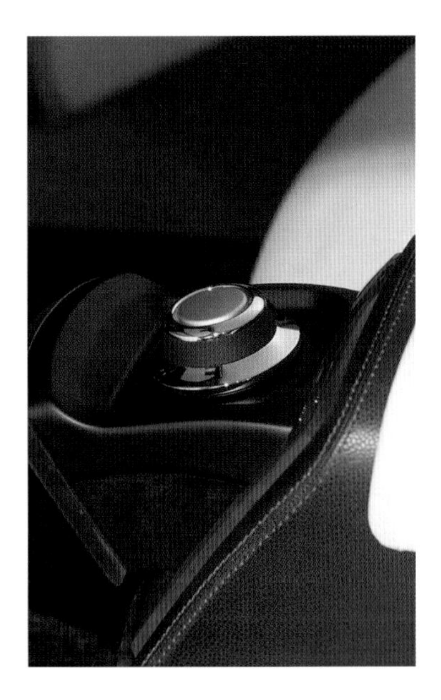

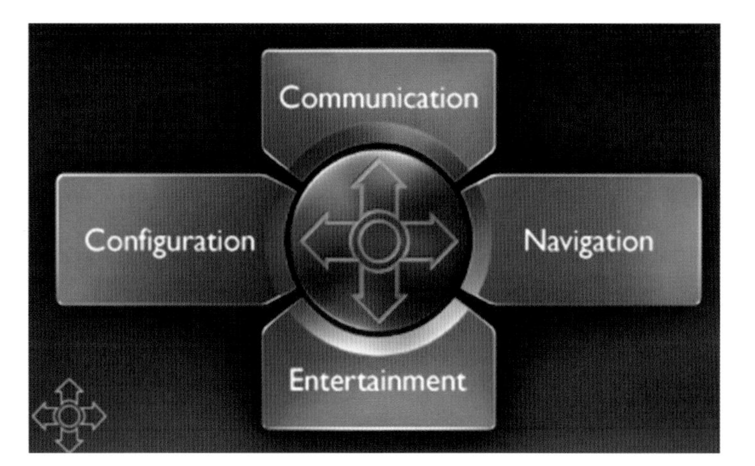

Above: the Controller emerges from the centre armrest, before providing a driver with the means to adjust communications, navigation, entertainment and vehicle configuration.

Above right: the 'Functionality upon request' screen display at the driver's service.

increase comfort and safety by enhancing the clarity of vision from within the car.

Much has already been written about the 'Authority Concept' and its 'Functionality upon request' element – the system by which the controls of secondary functions are concealed until needed. Technology has made this possible, for only a few years ago the complexities of designing and producing a reliable, workable Controller to select and choose the functions of communication, navigation, entertainment and vehicle configuration by one rotary switch would not have been possible.

Several of the secondary functions can be controlled by voice recognition. This is not a first in the motoring world, but now the Phantom's system is probably the most effective. Audio, telephone and navigation systems can be controlled in this manner, although the human touch is still an option. Rolls-Royce has taken the mass of potential control systems for the car and selected only those that really add to the car's ability to serve the driver and make his or her life easier.

Dr. Tim Leverton gave the Sir Henry Royce Memorial Lecture at the headquarters of the Institute of Mechanical Engineers in London on 6 November 2002. In it, he explained the major concepts which ensure the comfortable link between car and driver.

Advanced technology then ensured the transition from these concepts to reality, resulting in a car that was easy to operate and enjoyable to drive.

Advanced technology also made it possible to design and build the Phantom in such a short timespan. It was not that long ago that an adventurously designed car such as this would require a vast drawing office with draftsmen and tracers to laboriously create copy drawings. Components would then be made and tested, re-designed and re-tested until they were finally deemed satisfactory.

Today, with computer-aided design and manufacture (CAD/CAM), much of the testing can be done in a virtual world. When a component is finally produced for testing, it is almost certain to perform as expected.

The manufacturing process itself is, of course, technologically advanced. Even the painting of the bodyshells is a process that is infinitely more precise than was possible just a few years ago. The paint consists of chemicals with reduced environmental harm, and gives a richer, fuller colour to the surfaces covered. The computer-controlled booths and sprayguns reduce wastage and time, and minimise fumes. In fact, one can stand right next to the 'surface treatment' area in Goodwood, the equivalent of a paintshop in any other car plant, and be totally unaware that a highly volatile chemical process is underway.

The Phantom has sheet moulded plastic composite front wings. The reasons are threefold. The shape of the wing is too complex to be formed in metal by press tools. Several sections would have to be made separately. But, using a composite material, a single unit may be moulded. Secondly, the wings will have greater damage resistance. Lastly, the aerials for satellite navigation can be housed with no reduction in signal strength or interference from a metal wing. Sir Henry Royce would have approved!

BMW has made available its deep resources of technological know-how and mated it to the handcrafts synonymous with Rolls-Royce. The result is a car that looks, feels and smells like a Rolls-Royce, but also works like a car should at the cutting edge of automotive technology and uncompromising luxury.

Above: the clock housing panel will gently rotate upwards to reveal the Controller display screen.

Right: the range of information available is comprehensive but never confusing.

10 THE STORY OF ELEGANCE REGAINED

The ideas were plenty, but the skill needed was the exercise of judgement

– MAREK DJORDJEVIC

Opposite: rear lights use LED technology for faster response to braking and greater reliability than incandescent bulbs.

For Marek Djordjevic it was a dream come true – a chance to submit outline drawings and two scale models, against two competitors, for selection as exterior designer of the Phantom, which at that time in 1999 was known only as RR01. His remit at the beginning of that year was to start with a clean sheet of paper with no corporate preconceptions apart from three stipulations: RR01 had to have very large wheels, the famous radiator shell and, of course, the Spirit of Ecstasy mascot. Marek Djordjevic considered the problem, knowing that to create a car that was any sort of 'special BMW' just would not do. So he looked to past designs to understand what made a Rolls-Royce so special and easy to identify – even without seeing the very familiar front of the cars.

Three models of Rolls-Royce cars impressed him. The historic, iconic classic was the Silver Cloud. The contemporary classic, the understated car, was the Silver Shadow. And his favoured coachbuilt cars covered several different models and generations but were similar in being unique cars handbuilt by craftsmen. The inspiration of the Silver Cloud was easy to comprehend – possibly the one model most readily identifiable to the whole world as a Rolls-Royce. Likewise, the Silver Shadow was obviously acceptable as a quintessential example of restrained British style. The disparate third group, coachbuilt Rolls-Royce cars, spanned at least four decades, but Marek Djordjevic found he kept returning to the coachbuilt Phantom II of the early 1930s for his main inspiration for RR01.

He identified several key details of this car as classic Rolls-Royce signature elements. The sports Phantom II shown on page 51 is barely more than twice the height of its wheels. It has a very long wheelbase, with the front wheels well to the fore and a minimal front overhang of bodywork. There is a long bonnet and a massive expanse of metal along the side. The effect is finished off by a rising sweep of the door edge towards the front windscreen pillars. If one imagines a line drawn from rear to front along the lower edge of the body – along the edges of the running boards and mudguards – it rises gently to become a reflection of motion, even when stationary; a visual endorsement of 'waftability'. Another supporting theme was a chrome embellishment that ran from the radiator's side to the rear of the cabin in a gleaming, unbroken line. It is a reinforcement of the proportionate length of the car and the bonnet, that emphasises its gracefulness perfectly.

More formal Phantom IIs have elegant Sedanca de Ville bodies, an open fronted design, with contrasting, two-tone paint schemes or even material such as wickerwork applied to the body sides. Some of these two-dimensional designs only grace the back of the car and rear doors, others come forward to take in the front

Above: much of the Silver Cloud's styling, clear in this view, was combined with the coach doors of bespoke limousines on the Phantom.

Right: three variations on a theme, by exterior designer Marek Djordjevic.

Above: wheel size was a crucial element of the Phantom's design, tallying with the traditional measurement of being half the height of a Rolls-Royce.

doors. Marek Djordjevic would use this feature in vestigial fashion with a swaged line along RR01's sides.

Marek Djordjevic was further attracted to this period of early 1930s car design because it was a time when Rolls-Royce power was the force behind land, sea and air world speed records. RR01 was to have engineering superiority, not in terms of outright speed, but in the same attention to detail that enabled those record-holders to realise their goals. The design had to reflect that.

Referring back to the Silver Cloud, Marek Djordjevic noted the brightwork around the windscreen and the definitive front wing tops with shoulder lines moving forward to meet the bumper, parallel with and complimenting the vertical structure of the radiator. For the rear of RR01, inspiration was sought from such cars as a James Young-bodied Silver Wraith (see bottom picture, page 51) of the early 1950s. Its roofline descending towards the back, and the gentle separation away from that roofline and the rear quarter window, forming a large C-pillar, were strong elements. Cars like this also often featured forward-opening rear doors, for the elegant access they provided for passengers. This was deemed a similarly desirable attribute for the new Rolls-Royce by the design team, especially as it would be a unique feature among modern cars. However, later it became a headache for the engineers.

The team was fortunate to be allowed access to the fleet of cars belonging to the British Royal Family, kept in the Royal Mews at Buckingham Palace, where comparisons could be made to help assess the difference between British luxury cars and others in the global market, and also – importantly – the difference between Rolls-Royce and other British cars. It was becoming obvious to Djordjevic that there was a common story or theme behind the design of most Rolls-Royce coachwork.

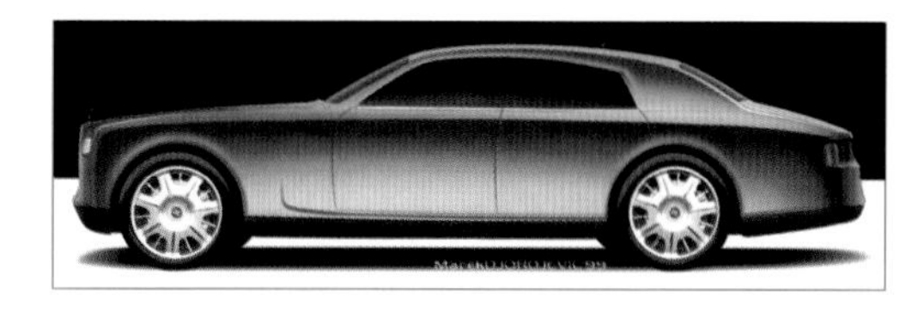

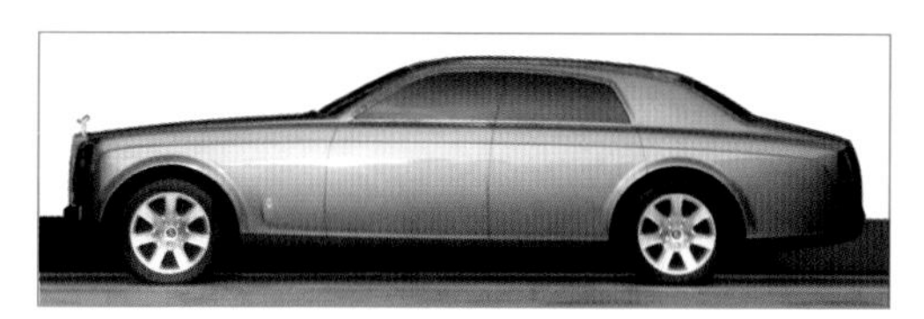

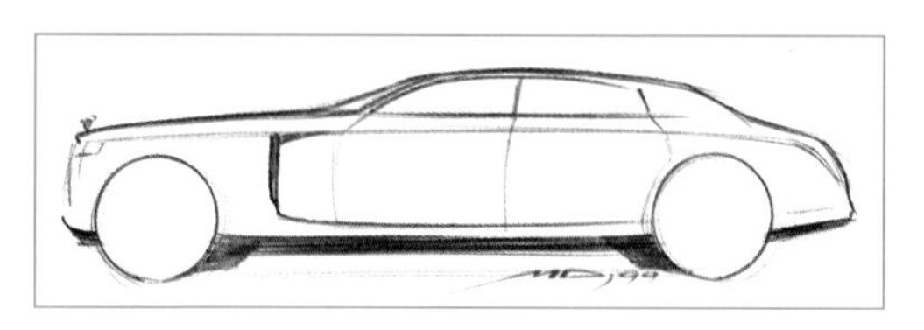

Earlier forms from the pen of designer Djordjevic – from left to right – close to the final version, an iteration with heritage more evident, and a thumbnail sketch.

With both doors open and, say, a chauffeur shielding the open-sided car, a sense of security is created.

RR

The Phantom's elegant rear proportions disappearing into the autumn landscape.

Opposite: there is no immediately obvious way to operate the door handle, yet grasp it lightly and you intuitively pull it open gently.

"The front starts very powerfully, with a great deal of presence and statesmanship," he explains. "As your eye goes towards the back of the car, the design gently gets 'quieter' and more demure. Finally, at the rear, it is very restrained, very elegant."

Armed with so much research, Marek Djordjevic was now ready to start sketching his final version, and it would incorporate all the items he saw as essential to an absolutely authentic Rolls-Royce design. Even his initial sketches were amazingly close to the final iteration, including the overall proportions, the dynamic main lines of the car, the run of the sill, the roofline and doors.

"As the scale models and then the full-size version began to take shape, we were very proud that we had retained the purity of the design throughout the process," he recalls. Marek's presentation was accepted by the board of BMW in December 1999. Project Rolls-Royce now had a form for its vision, and chief designer Ian Cameron puts the process into perspective. "From sketches to scale models and then full-sized models in less than a year is phenomenally quick. It usually takes much longer than that."

There is always a degree of tension between designers and engineers. Indeed, for Ian Cameron there were some difficulties in implementing aspects of the exterior design. He remembers well how the forward-opening coach doors gave the most headaches. "In purely legislative car design terms, this feature was no longer allowed, so if you based the uniqueness of the car on it, and invested a great deal of time on making the doors legally permissible, and it was still rejected – well, then you would really be up the creek without a paddle."

To make the most of the rear-hinged door, the rear floor had to be flat. The Phantom's spaceframe has a double floor with all the parts that normally necessitate a transmission tunnel and footwells, tucked neatly between the layers.

"Yes, it's a door that looks like a door, not a sort of hatch," says Cameron. "But you have to use it in a certain way. It's like getting on a horse: if you get on the wrong way, you will fall off. You must walk forward into this car, and then walk out of it."

Cameron explained it was not enough to prove the door could be made safe with electronic interlocks and the like; it also had to offer a distinct advantage in the minds of the legislators. What made it acceptable in the end was that, with both a front and rear door open, and with a chauffeur or bodyguard at the doors' outer edges, a passenger could be safely protected. Such is the world in which the Phantom has made its entrance!

In many of the early sketches and simulations there was no 'B' pillar at all between front and rear door windows. This effect always looks rakish, but often causes insurmountable problems in terms of side impact crash legislation. This was the case for RR01, and the decision was taken to make a feature of the 'B' pillar rather than try hard to conceal such a fixture. It is intended to be a visible confirmation of the side impact strength of the car; it also contains "some of the climate control and air-conditioning ducts," according to Marek Djordjevic.

He has successfully incorporated those three immutable elements within his design: big wheels, radiator, and mascot. The car looks imposing and inviting from a distance. As well as the cues from pre-war Rolls-Royce models, there are pleasing hints of Silver Cloud to its overall silhouette. Marek has included such historic and harmonious details throughout. Yet no one element is 'retro' in this design. The entire car features proportions and elements merely inspired by the best of the past. Marek Djordjevic had to reinterpret those elements to be up-to-date, sometimes even futuristic. He had to create a shape and include details that would be just as timeless in 10 years as they are today.

From the rear, there is a lot of Silver Cloud influence, with a splash of Silver Seraph too. Perhaps there is most 'Cloud' from the rear three-quarter angle view because the waistline separates the upper and lower halves of the car so dramatically. On the distinctive side of the Phantom, the chrome line from the radiator to the rear of the cabin is a homage to the Phantom II, and the lower swage line is the vestigial reminder of Marek Djordjevic's favourite wickerwork decoration on the bodies of the 1930s-built cars, even to the point where one of the paint choices features a contrasting lower panel that emphasises the swage line. Viewed from the front three-quarters position, the brightwork of the bonnet divider and the prominent, domed top edge to the wing are characteristic features of every previous Rolls-Royce from the Silver Cloud III to the Silver Seraph. Head-on, however, the radiator shell is much larger than those on earlier models and really dominates the front.

The detail sculpting of the front panels on the composite wings does much to reduce the impression of flatness suggested in some pictures.

Although rectangular lamps have been used on Rolls-Royce cars since the Silver Spirit arrived in 1980, the Phantom's rendering of upper rectangular running lights and indicators, positioned above the round headlamps, does look unusual – less conventionally graceful than the rest of the car, especially in photographs. In reality, when one can see the form of the front panels in more detail, it all makes more sense and rests easier on the eye.

John Blatchley is a man of impeccable Rolls-Royce credentials. In the 1930s, he worked as a designer for coachbuilder Gurney Nutting, which produced some of the most exotic and stylish bodies of the time. His war years were spent working on Rolls-Royce aircraft development, after which he moved to the Car Division, where he became the company's first in-house designer – a career that culminated with the 1965 Silver Shadow. At the beginning of 2000, the design team arranged to visit the spritely 90-year old. They took with them sketches and photographs of the six contenders for RR01's exterior design including the car already signed off for production and too late to change. Blatchley looked through the folder without comment, closed it and put it aside, saying quietly: "There is only one Rolls-Royce here."

Marek Djordjevic was desperate to know which design he was referring to because he was mightily impressed by the old man. "The amazing thing was his visual perception, the clarity of design, his ability to pick up on detail and so forth, had not deteriorated to that day," says Djordjevic. "His ability to perceive things 'visually' was better than a man a third his age."

Marek Djordjevic could wait no longer and Blatchley was enjoying his tease. In the end, he picked up the book and pointed to Djordjevic's own design, repeating: "There is only one Rolls-Royce here."

Two schools of thought are proposed for many endeavours in this world: 'paint with a broad brush' and 'the devil's in the detail'. Marek Djordjevic adheres to both maxims because the Phantom is equally impressive from a distance and close-up. Components such as door handles are beautifully shaped and constructed, reflecting in their way the overall theme of the entire car. As with all exterior brightwork a chromium plated finish is used, the quality of which allows the term 'mirror finish' to be used without qualification.

While Marek and his group worked, two of Ian Cameron's other team members were matching paint colours and combinations. They were allowed a palette

The Phantom powers its way through a climbing turn in Santa Barbara with balanced ease. This car features an upper and lower two-tone paintwork scheme.

of 24 colour choices, nine single and 15 duo-tones for the standard range, although the versatile, state-of-the-art paint facility at Goodwood can create several thousand colours from its basic paint range.

Two optional colour schemes are available from the standard one-colour finish. First, 'upper two-tone' which features the upper bootlid, roof and bonnet in the same contrasting colour as the sills, the rest of the car being in the main-choice colour; as with earlier cars, Rolls-Royce recommends the lighter colour to be on top, although they are pleased to take the customers' instructions on the matter.

The second option is 'side two-tone', where the whole car including the sills is painted in the main choice, with the contrasting colour applied to the lower sides, rising to and contained by the swaged line. This choice is most redolent of the cars with wickerwork application that so impressed designer Marek Djordjevic. A single coachline can be applied running beneath the brightwork from radiator to 'C' pillar. A double line of the same colour can enhance the body contour from front wing to rear. Those customers whose preference is for the side two-tone can have it contained within a coachline. The ever-upright linked R-R symbol in the wheel centres are contained within a painted surround which either matches the body colour, or the contrast colour, if appropriate.

As already stated, there is always a battle between designers and engineers, so would Marek Djordjevic's design be susceptible to wind noise and side winds, and what sort of coefficient of drag – the mathematical description of its wind-resistance – would it possess? The old adage 'if it looks right, it is right' once again came to the rescue. Wind noise was well within expectations and side-wind deviation was remarkably good. All the car needed now was an interior design as striking as Marek's exterior. In the event, Charles Coldham not only supplied that need, but achieved it in total sympathy with the exterior – such serendipity Ian Cameron knew is not always the case.

11 THE COMFORT ZONE: INSIDE THE PHANTOM

Small things make perfection, but perfection is no small thing

– SIR HENRY ROYCE

Opposite: sumptuous seating is separated by an armrest containing cubby, electric seat controls and, behind a wooden cover, the Controller.

Alongside the other creative teams working at the Bank was one whose specific remit was to create the interior design for RR01. Its members were competing against each other with ideas, and the person whose concept was deemed to be the best fit with the ethos of the car would see their work realised. He or she would be invited to join the main design team to work towards the final, completed iteration of the Phantom.

A luxury car must score highly in every area to command a premium price over lesser offerings, but the interior must truly be something special. The Rolls-Royce designers knew the interior of their new car would have to feature the traditional, high-quality materials of English coachbuilding, such as leather, wood and Wilton-style carpets. But the ambience of past models was to be expressed in a totally up-to-date manner. The creators of the interior had to break new ground because their designs would also have to cater for the housing and concealment of the secondary control systems, as well as creature comforts made practical by modern technology.

Every one of the design proposals made by the team at the Bank demonstrated a desire to take the design of the traditional British bespoke car interior forward into the 21st century. Dyed-in-the-wool Rolls-Royce owners may have a liking for the simple, old-fashioned facia interpretation of the Silver Dawn/Bentley Mk.VI but many other themes were tried; nautical, Art Deco, aeronautical and ultra-modern were some examples. In the end, however, the winning design by ex-Rover designer Charles Coldham deserved to have been chosen. His carefully crafted work must surely appeal to the traditional owner weaned on the Silver Cloud or Silver Shadow as much as the new owner wanting something with an extra dimension above and beyond any other luxury car already on sale.

Take a quick glance inside the Phantom and one would be forgiven for thinking one had glimpsed a 'current' interior by one of the great coachbuilders of the past – if not HJ Mulliner or Park Ward, then James Young or Hooper could surely have been responsible, had they still been trading today. Experienced Rolls-Royce owners will immediately feel at home because of the surface coverings of deep-pile carpet, leather and wood veneer, and they will also recognise the chromium eyeball air vents with their 'organ stop' controls and the familiar gear selection indicator – first seen in the Silver Shadow.

The violin tuning key-style switches are a reminder of the Silver Cloud, while the switchbox for operating the starter and lights is a direct reinterpretation of the same detail found since the 20hp model introduced in 1922. The speedometer design is truly reminiscent of every Rolls-Royce produced since the

RESET

The facia houses few visible controls – all part of the 'Functionality upon request' concept of secondary controls remaining hidden until needed.

1930s, although now of course with a tamper-proof digital odometer.

One might possibly suspect these 'styling cues' have been included solely to enhance nostalgia for the traditional Rolls-Royce values within the new car. Not so. Chief designer Ian Cameron makes the point that considerable research went into the relevant dimensions and styling features that have appeared in earlier Rolls-Royce models over the last 70 or so years. Obviously much of the data was not pertinent for a brand new design built in 2003 but, once the designers had what was thought to be the distilled essence that made a Rolls-Royce unique, it was built into the Phantom. In some instances, like the eyeball air vents, they just proved to be the very best designs for their job. Why change something just for change's sake and detract from its functionality?

Tastes change. A style or material considered the absolute epitome of good taste or, indeed, bad taste in one age can easily reverse polarity with the passing of time. Never more so than in today's world, where the need to sell new products forces unnecessary change upon us. Fortunately, many people are not prepared to accept this. They choose products to suit the function, products made to last, products manufactured from timeless materials. These materials may, however, be brand new: who would argue that carbon fibre or heat-resistant ceramics are worthless? Or they may be traditional: wood – real wood – is better suited to certain applications. In the Phantom there is an undeniable affinity for the use of certain traditional materials. Beautifully finished, natural wood and leather remain unsurpassed as the ultimate materials for the interior finishing of an English luxury motor car.

Designer Coldham certainly felt this, for he built on the established use of leather with zeal. Between 15 and 18 hides are needed to cover surfaces such as seats, doors and associated trim panels, with the striking use of differently textured surfaces.

These hides were chosen by Sandy McGill at BMW Group's Designworks Concept Studio in California in her role as colour and material coordinator. She chose to employ a natural grain for the seats and a textured 'tipped' leather for doors and centre consoles. Tipped leather has an embossed grain to it that is better suited to hard wearing surfaces. Areas that would otherwise be

Designer Charles Coldham's interpretation of a facia reminiscent of the later Silver Dawn from the 1950s.

prone to shrinkage in sunlight, such as the facia-top roll, are pre-shrunk. The Phantom boasts the softest leather hides in the car industry: as hard-wearing as any used in cars, it is as supple as aniline leather used in the clothing industry. This softness is achieved by a new 'drum pigmentation' process that distributes the colour right through the hide, allowing the feel and look of the natural material to remain undiminished. As a side issue, the expected 'creaking' of traditionally finished leather can no longer be heard; this is probably due more than anything else to the incredible rigidity of the spaceframe construction, which reduces the inherent flexing of the moving car.

Sandy McGill's final selection included 15 hide colours which she evolved into 19 combinations falling into two main groups: The 'Mono' group utilises leather and carpeting of one colour, while the 'Contrast' combinations use the primary colour for the seats, main door panels and console covers, with an additional, complementary colour to carpets, door panniers and centre consoles.

One problem for production engineer Alan Sheppard to tackle was to ensure the chosen materials would be suitable for their specific purposes. Wonderful as the headlining material may be, if it sags in hot climates, or the pattern warps on fixing, then it is simply no good. If the leather will not stretch around the form of a sharp corner, or it creases on inside curves, then it, too, is not suitable. And if a selected wood has a grain that is too short for its application, an alternative solution would have to be found.

These and other challenges having been met, designers Sami Coultas and Kris Sukhu had the important task of quality control to attend to. The problem of colour-coordinating hides, carpets and other textiles is ongoing. Paint finishes are also under their eagle eyes. They can spot a difference in shade, tone or hue that would be beyond most of us. They both instinctively demonstrate the visual equivalent of 'perfect pitch'.

The steering wheel is leather-bound with internal hemming, making the surface perfectly smooth and

Above: the overhead interior lights are a triumph of style and function.

Right: rear compartment climate controls surmounted by a pair of air vents.

comfortably tactile. The headlining has a leather centre section flanked by blended wool/cashmere panels, all in a single colour to co-ordinate with all of the interior tones. Coldham included traditional leather 'grab' straps with spring returns – now officially entitled 'Duchess straps' – which can be found in their traditional positions, high up on the inside of the 'C' pillars and above the front occupants' side windows.

Carpets are purchased from an outside vendor as the relatively small production run at Goodwood does not warrant the large investment Rolls-Royce would need to make to weave its own. The carpets themselves are, of course, colour-matched and made from high-density looped wool. Being cut and formed for shape and trimmed for height of pile, they are all held in place by solid trim frames, which eliminates the need for leather welts.

Coldham did have abundant scope for innovative design, as there was all the Phantom's modern technology to be housed in line with the demands of 'Authority' and 'Functionality upon request' concepts. In practical terms, this amounted to working with the engineers who, for example, did their best to house unsightly items such as seat adjusters and the Controller in the front central armrest while, for his part, Coldham designed an armrest in sympathy with his overall concept, one capable of containing and giving easy access to everything inside it.

Innovation has also been included for design reasons alone; the doors' vertical storage bins, for instance, proud of the main door trims, are surmounted by wood cappings with definitive curves. There are footrests in the rear beneath the lambswool over-rugs, that fold flat into floor recesses. Most stylish of all are the front and rear roof lamps. They provide four levels of lighting: 'ambience' uses tiny LEDs to highlight small areas of the interior; 'boulevard' gives soft lighting to aid conversation on the move; reading lights are provided on either side for rear seat passengers; and 'full lighting' illuminates entry and exit from the car.

But it is the design of these central overhead lamps that is so pleasing. Their pale green frosted glass has layered curves to the front in the fashion of gentle waves petering out on a tropical beach. The glass is divided by a matt black control panel, set in a chrome surround. The whole thing could have been stolen from the RMS Queen Mary – except for the state-of-the-art control panel. These lights are complemented by quarterlight

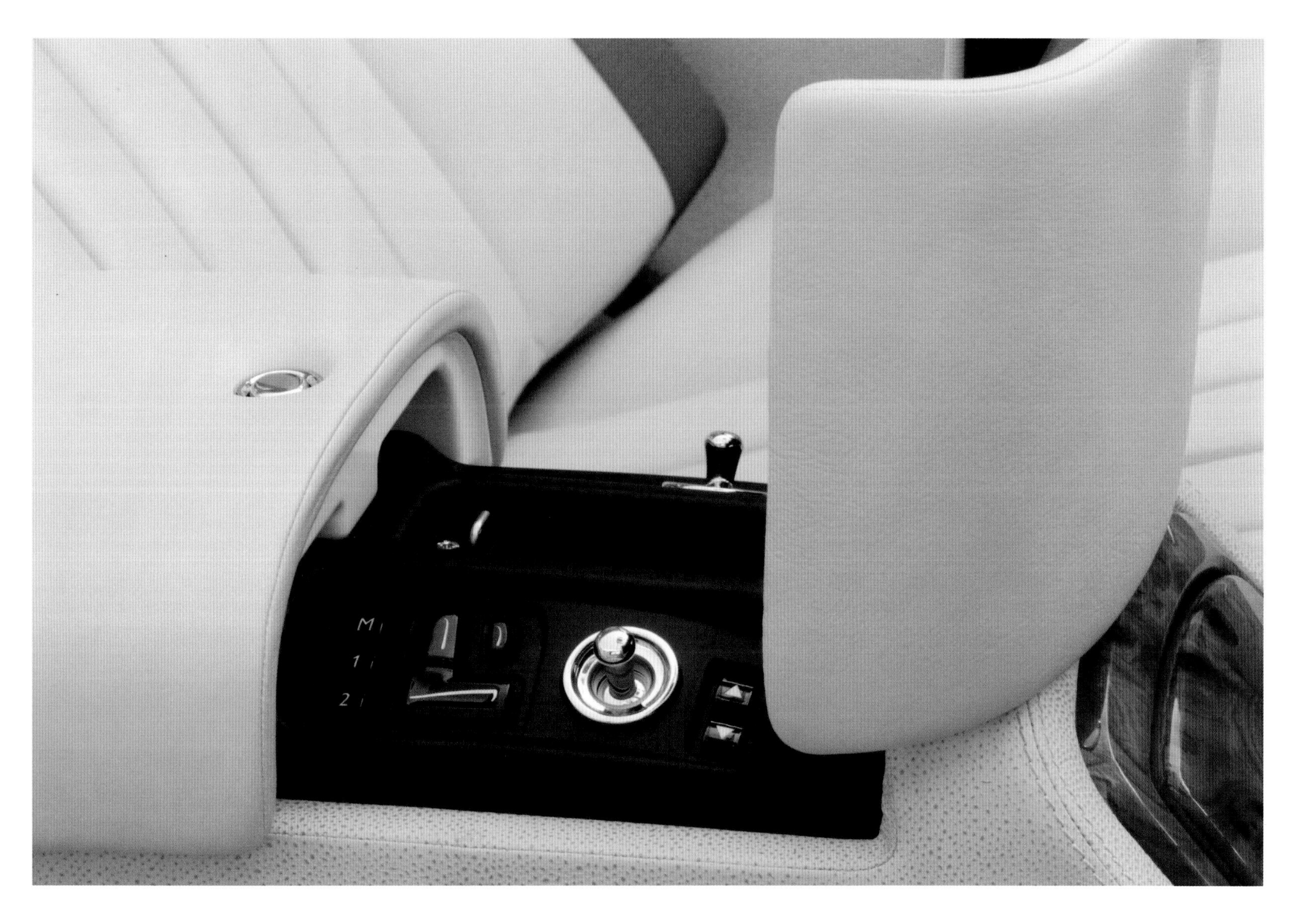

The centre armrest cubby reveals its secrets. The controls adjust the front seat configuration.

mirrors on the 'C' pillars, as in all Rolls-Royce motor cars since the Silver Dawn, only now they are positioned a little too far back for personal use. In fact, they are designed to create a sense of space and light – whatever setting is chosen.

At Coldham's insistence, straight grained woods are used on horizontal surfaces and figured grains on vertical surfaces, adding contrast and visual appeal. Customers can choose from woods including figured mahogany, burr walnut, bird's eye maple, black tulip, oak burr and elm cluster. Of course, should customers require inlay work or painted veneers, these can be supplied by arrangement. The look and feel of the wood in the Phantom is very different to the decorative, stuck-on appliqué that passes for 'real' wood on many other modern cars. That surface covering often becomes two-dimensional and shaped into unnatural contours for wood. In the Phantom, wood is used as an architectural element, in true cabinet-making ways.

All of the chromium-finished parts within the interior have one of two finishes. There is a satin-finish for a setting, backing or bezel and a polished-finish for any control that requires manual operation.

The front seats are everything a driver or passenger could want. They are large, comfortable and supportive with a plethora of adjustments to allow a driver of any size to take advantage of the 'Authority Concept'. Traditional in appearance, with fluted panels and solid outer bolster panels, they are easy to enter and leave. The back seats are supplied in two offerings. 'Lounge

Above: close but no cigar! A step in the design process that became the first version.

Right: compare the proposed version to this, a pre-production interior.

SELECT
SERVICE
PANEL
AUTO

Traditional Rolls-Royce switchbox now sports a 'Starter' button for the first time in almost fifty years. 'P' button engages the automatic Parking Brake.

configuration' is a comfortable update on the traditional Rolls-Royce style, probably closest to a Silver Cloud's except for an increased wraparound at the sides to make relaxed conversation easier and save cricked necks when facing towards the front of the car. 'Individual configuration' sports a fixed central armrest and console with storage space inside. An optional upgrade of this is the 'theatre configuration', the same basic layout but with the armrest containing any entertainment choice from a DVD player to a Champagne chiller, available upon customer request. In both cases, the twin rear seats have as much powered adjustment as those in front. A small point featured within the 'Authority Concept' is the slightly raised height of the rear seat over the front, allowing passengers in the back to see out through the windscreen more easily. As exterior designer Marek Djordjevic wanted from the outset, all the occupants should be able to see and admire the Spirit of Ecstasy!

Mentioned in several previous chapters are the forward-opening, rear coach doors. Their effectiveness in aiding the graceful and comfortable entry to and exit from the car is best understood by studying the car or a photograph of it. Once seated, there is a delightful choice of leaning forward to pull the door closed, using the door pull set into the window rail, or pressing a button set into the rear door pillar, which shuts the door automatically. All doors and the bootlid have their final few millimetres of closing travel completed electrically; this is called 'soft closing'. A small feature, but a useful one, is that all doors have infinite stops, with no set detents – in other words, they stay open at any chosen angle.

The flat rear floor allows full use of the coach doors' accessibility. The passengers do not have to carefully place their feet with ankles at an awkward angle and toes pushed against the transmission tunnel. They can take their seat as easily as in a favourite armchair and, of course, move to the other side of the car with ease when lounge seating is specified. If any doubts prevail as to the benefit of a flat floor, then take a long journey in a car with footwells which limit the movement of feet and legs.

If it is raining at the beginning or end of a Phantom journey, passengers will be grateful to find an umbrella contained in each rear door. With either a front or rear

Top left: the Rolls-Royce ideal of an American institution – the cupholder, above which can be seen the switches for the electrically heated seats.

Top right: two of the Logic7™ speakers situated next to the sterling chrome-finished door handles, surround and polished chrome controls.

Above: the mirrors in the rear 'C' pillars are not designed for personal use – they are there to reflect a sense of space and light.

door open, these Teflon-coated, moisture and mildew resistant additions to the Phantom's attributes can be pulled from their storage compartments just below the door lock mechanisms. For any unforeseen fate of a rather worse nature, with the touch of a button mounted in the headliner, the Rolls-Royce Motor Cars Assist Centre could be dialled and any problem dealt with. If the air bags are deployed, the Centre would be automatically informed of an emergency. This Assist system should be fully operational for selected European and North American markets in the near future.

Adverse comments have been made in relation to a few minor points. The door pulls set into the window rails are fixed inside at their bases by ugly crosshead screws. It is not difficult to imagine an elegant hand catching a finely manicured nail or two on these fixings. The front seats have a sterling-finished trim at the outer edge of their bases, which does not possess the same reflection as the rest of the interior brightwork. The rear seats are set on a leather-covered hard base, the corners of which are slightly proud of the seats themselves; when sliding forward to leave the car, these corners may suffer wear and tear to a noticeable degree. Aside from these small points, any other criticism would be merely a matter of personal taste.

Coldham has translated the Project Rolls-Royce brief most effectively. He had the advantage of time spent with Land Rover teaching him the skill of interior design on a large scale, while working on the Land Rover Discovery. Overall, it is extremely difficult to see how a better meld of traditional and contemporary design could have been achieved for a luxury car interior. Obviously, it could have been different, but it would not have been superior.

Part 3

MAKING THE PHANTOM A REALITY

12 THE PRODUCTION LINE: HOW THE PHANTOM COMES TOGETHER

Whatever is rightly done, however humble, is noble – SIR HENRY ROYCE

Opposite: smartly dressed in their anti-scratch outfits, line workers mate body and subframe with the mechanical elements of the Phantom.

The Project Rolls-Royce manufacturing team had an immutable date seared in their collective mind: New Year's Eve, 2002. This was when the first customer was to take delivery of his Phantom. The objective was successfully accomplished and by January 2004, with the 500th Phantom completed and production soon to reach the company's maximum annual capacity of 1000 cars a year, they could be satisfied that the entire manufacturing plant worked perfectly. The story of how this was achieved is covered in later chapters; here, however, the assembly of the Phantom is explained.

It begins with the arrival at Goodwood of the bodyshells which travel by transporter trucks from the BMW Group's specialist aluminium spaceframe construction facilities in Dingolfing in Germany. After being checked for any imperfections, they start their journey through the 'surface treatment centre' – the paint shop.

Dieter Udelhoven, who was at the time head of manufacturing, explains: "Here, we have a new process which uses semi-automated paint booths. Each car is painted in its chosen colour – even two-tones – and the shell moves from booth to booth on a conveyor system."

When the paint process is complete, the car is pushed by hand on its trolley to a holding area to await its turn on the production line. When that time comes, it is once again manually pushed to the beginning of the line.

Each bodyshell has a number, which corresponds to a customer order, so, even at this early stage, a car can be identified. The car, of course, will later receive a vehicle identification number (VIN), but that will not be attached until the car reaches station five of the 19 stations on the line. Should a car have special fitments, that might hold up the flow of the production line, it can be pushed to the side to await attention. The speed of the Phantom production line is snail-like by normal automotive industry standards, but there is much to do at each stage and the carefully timed multiple tasks to be performed by each skilled operative cannot be hurried or skimped. Quality control is all pervading.

The first tasks to be undertaken on the bodyshell are the wiring and soundproofing, and the fitting of the chromium-plated bonnet divider. Pre-assembled components are added, one of the most impressively-engineered of which is the single-piece magnesium alloy instrument panel carrier. The drivetrain, consisting of everything from radiator to rear axle, is assembled on a separate jig frame which is then wheeled on tracks to the underside of the body, where the two elements are joined.

To the left of the pre-assembly area is the logistics area, or stores which supplies the production line with the necessary parts. Relatively few sets of components are stored, as a condition of the planning consent for the

Door interior trim is completed, using a custom-made jig for accuracy.

site limits the number of large lorries inwards and outwards to 20 per day. By having the main Rolls-Royce logistics centre based at Oxford, 60 miles away from Goodwood, the production line is currently fed by only seven trucks a day. This makes considerably less of an environmental impact than that caused by the nearby supermarket's transport requirements!

After the installation of most of the major elements such as air-conditioning, electronics and front and rear screens, the doors – which had been separated from the body after painting – are now reunited with it. They have been fitted with windows and all their electric winding mechanisms, plus corresponding locks and handles. Finally, they have received their wood and leather trim.

During this assembly process, they have been transported around the assembly area on upright jigs with protective sides. Indeed, enormous care is taken to avoid even the slightest scratch on any part of the car. The cars are given wing and body side covers, while the workforce wear cleverly designed clothing with concealed fastenings. There are also compulsory protective visitor's coats for any visitors to the line who, like the workforce, must remove all jewellery and watches.

Sub-assemblies, such as the engine, can be manufactured most efficiently at BMW's existing facilities: setting up duplicate machine shops and test beds in Goodwood was never contemplated or considered necessary. However, it is unlikely that the heritage and skills of working with wood and leather for car interiors could be surpassed outside England. Perhaps, of all the attributes appreciated in a Rolls-Royce, it is the quality and use of these two natural materials that makes a lasting impression on the senses of sight, touch and in the latter's case, smell. The final assembly of the interior, therefore, is the most crucial one, and also the culmination of a long and varied set of processes within the leather and wood shops.

Leather hides held in stock at Rolls-Royce have already been chosen from the very best available. Rolls-Royce uses only the hides of bulls. Apparently, the cows' ability to stretch their skins when carrying calves makes them less suitable for use in automotive interiors – the cowhide would tend to pucker when wrapped around tight corners! The hides are checked by hand and eye for

A computerised robotic spraygun finishes a Phantom's coachwork far better than human hand and eye could ever achieve.

any blemishes, which are marked for avoidance before the leather is stretched out on to a vacuum frame prior to laser-guided cutting.

The pattern for each of the 450 required pieces can be repositioned by computer to maximise the use of individual hides and to work around the marked blemishes. The cut pieces, with small triangular tabs for stitch alignment, are then skived (or shaved) along their edges if they are to be folded before stitching. Complete panels are skived if they are to cover hard surfaces without any padding.

Eduard Wenner, manager of interior trim, leather and wood, explained that these operations were a perfect example of established techniques being retained while embracing the very latest technology. Certainly, to see a piece of leather being fed into a computerised, self-sharpening skiver that can reduce the material's thickness by tenths of a millimetre is extremely impressive. The use of traditional sewing machines and hand-finishing are maintained because they are skills that cannot be matched by automation. Absolute quality control when leather panels are stitched over air bags, for example, is paramount, yet the sewing machines for these items are operated by people, with computer monitoring only as a back-up to their innate skills.

The stitching and thread used on these airbag

facings is weaker than those used elsewhere on the car so that, upon activation, the air bags can burst through them without fear of either deployment being restrained, or of flying leather lashing the faces of occupants. Every reel of thread has a bar code, a copy of which is embossed on the rear of the finished leather. In the event of a crash which results in details of the airbag deployment being analysed, all of the trim components can be traced.

For all leather surfaces, stitched or unstitched, thermo-sensitive water based glues are employed for manually attaching the leather to base materials, whether it is padding, metal or wood. So good is the fume extraction equipment in the plant for these glues that the water collected as a byproduct is used for pot plants around the leather shop offices; so far, all of them have enjoyed a natural life span!

The Goodwood wood shop is as bright and spotless as the rest of the manufacturing plant. The environmentally friendly air-conditioning keeps wood dust and adhesive fumes to almost zero. The highly skilled craftsmen work with six different types of wood. Forty wooden panels are made up, containing up to fifteen layers of wafer-thin wood, each one interspersed with three layers of glue film. There are also at least two layers of aluminium to aid crashworthiness and to help retain the rigid form of the finished component. The completed sections are pressed and heated for a few minutes to activate the glue. Waste material is cut away and the part-finished item is sanded before suitable surface veneers are glued into place. In this case, 'suitable' means matched perfectly throughout the car.

Again, waste material is trimmed and the perfectly-shaped item is sanded to form a smooth surface. Eduard Wenner explained that, because of environmental sensitivity on the Goodwood site, the final gloss finish is applied elsewhere because the process generates some fumes. Both leather and wood 'sets' for each individual car are produced as a batch, production only starting when the bodyshell is ready for painting.

The car is now ready for the painstaking processes of starting, wheel-alignment and the multitude of checks and settings the on-board computer-monitored systems require. Every completed Phantom undergoes a 'squeak, rattle and roll' test, where microphones check for the slightest noise when the car's torsional rigidity is assessed.

There is a dedicated test area for cars fitted with

A Phantom body is readied for what Rolls-Royce calls 'surface treatment' – which means painting.

Opposite: a leather worker sets up laser patterns to avoid blemishes and gain maximum use of each hide.

Above: a seamstress uses well-honed skills to create perfect stitching.

Right: a special computer-guided cutting tool creates leather pieces according to laser patterns.

customer-specified non-standard electrical equipment, such as in-car entertainment systems. This equipment needs careful, individual integration to correct any faults and ensure that it does not conflict with any other system. A 'lab car', or test jig, has been built that the company uses for this work and also to test the suitability of any new electrical components that might be fitted to all Phantoms. Apart from looking vaguely like a real car, it contains all the electrical equipment from a completely standard Phantom.

When every assembly task is completed, each car is driven and signed off as being free of faults, it is cocooned in a heat-shrink wrapped cover. A soft plastic zip gives entry to the driver's door and a small 'window' allows transport drivers to manoeuvre the car. It can now be delivered to a dealership, or moved to the customer collection room attached to the office wing at the plant – from where its journey into the life of a lucky new owner can truly begin.

13 MAKING SENSE OF A LOGISTICS WEB

A horse! a horse! my kingdom for a horse – WILLIAM SHAKESPEARE

Opposite: door trim panels ready to be fitted.

Logistics, the age-old problem of having the right parts, in the right quantities, in the right place, at the right time, can be a challenge. In the case of a car manufacturer, not enough of an item and the production line will stop or, at the very least, cars will have to be side-tracked to await their missing parts; too many items and unnecessary purchase, handling and storage costs are incurred. Rolls-Royce Motor Cars has the added issue that its Goodwood plant is situated in a conservation area which is environmentally-sensitive. This restricts the company to a maximum of 20 heavy commercial vehicle movements in any 24-hour period. Of course, with the present output of five or six cars per day, the problems could be more onerous. Many suppliers do not deliver in tiny batches, so a holding area – some sort of halfway house – was needed, and that is based near Oxford.

In general terms, Henry Ford's adoption of mass production, which he devised after seeing a mass dismantling process for cattle at the Chicago stockyards, evolved long ago into the type of production system known today as 'just in time'. In the early days of mass-production, large numbers of each component were held at the assembly line where, if the part did not fit, it would be returned or put aside for re-use when it did – the aim was to make as many units as possible, and not to be held up by parts supply issues. By comparison, the 'just in time' system assures that if, for instance, 60 cars go down the line in an hour, a corresponding 60 examples of a given component are there to be fitted. In terms of Rolls-Royce, the way the Phantom has been engineered at the design phase, and the fact that the external component suppliers are instilled with a right-first-time ethos, has already reduced the reject rate virtually to zero. This allows much greater quality control at each step of the car's construction. Tony Gott elaborates, "Parts from BMW are 'just in time' because, with an internal control system, it is the best option. For other components, there is a commercial discussion about the batch size, but excess stocks will be held elsewhere."

Holger Groitzsch oversees the logistics at Rolls-Royce Motor Cars. He explains the particular problem that Rolls-Royce has, and the solution. "We have to talk business with suppliers who are used to supplying 100,000 parts per year in batches of thousands. So a single production run for us, may well supply the parts for a whole year's worth of Phantoms. Where to store them all, not to mention the obsolescence that any change in technical specification may cause, would lead to a very unhappy accounts department.

The answer to this efficient logistical management, in a case such as ours, is in our Programme Planning approach. We build cars to match individual customer orders. Each of these customers can choose from a vast

7618

An engine and gearbox waiting to meet the rest of the drivetrain, on a trolley. Note the first-stage exhaust expansion box.

selection of features on the options and bespoke design lists. Not only is it a challenge to cope with the items on these lists, but we have to maintain a reasonable delivery time - and reasonable for us is as low as four weeks. We can succeed by treating each car as an individual project, which must be controlled with the highest degree of accuracy. Failure anywhere will have severe consequences. Remember, a delay in the building of one car in a day represents 20% of our production. Try to find a mass car maker who can cope with a 20% deviation in its daily programme."

The clear structure of logistics within the manufacturing plant was devised by then head of manufacturing, Dieter Udelhoven and his team. Materials flow into the building from the eastern side. There is sufficient storage space for about five days' production, utilising computerised storage bins up to six stacks high. When a designated bodyshell begins its journey through the paint shop, all the required parts for that particular car must be available. It was designed so that the distance from the stores area to the sub-assembly line is a matter of a few metres, and the distance from there to the main production line is similarly short. The fact that the operatives working in the stores, the sub-assembly area and the main production line can all see one another helps everyone feel part of an integrated process.

Logistics organisation can be helped somewhat by

Completed and tested, Phantoms in their protective, heat-shrunk cocoons, await the start of their delivery journeys.

the engineering designs. Tim Leverton, chief engineer explains, "With the volume of production being so low, the control points in the manufacturing process had to be carefully specified. There is, in fact, pretty much 100 per cent inspection and quality assurance. Deciding on the parameters that had to be met was, obviously, a fundamental part of building up the requirements for our external suppliers. That was achieved by initiating a quality division within the engineering department and extending its reach into the manufacturing process. Intimate involvement with the design engineering process and parallel discussions with the suppliers allowed us to agree standards early on."

Logistical issues reach beyond the building of the Phantom. Once delivered to their owners across the world, they have to be maintained and possibly repaired when damaged. The accepted method of parts storage would be at the premises of the various dealerships, but Rolls-Royce Motor Cars does things differently. Apart from service consumables – parts that are either time – or mileage-replaceable, all major spares and replacement parts, are stored at the Oxford hub. Today, the reliability of worldwide courier services mean parts can be dispatched and arrive no later than four days just about anywhere in the world. This is attractive for the dealerships because limited inventory means they do not need to tie up capital, and owners are assured that exactly the right part will be available for their

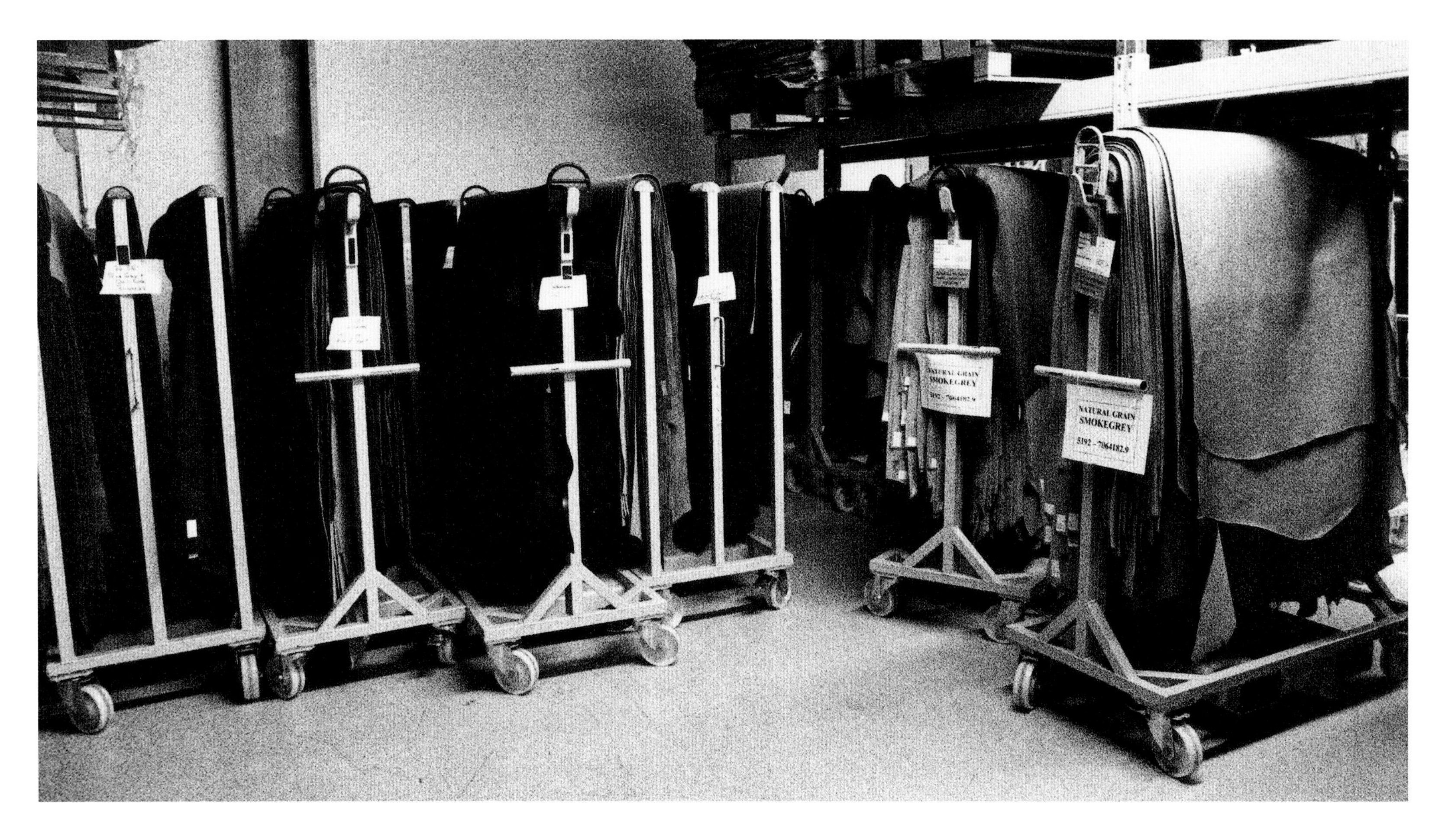

Hides awaiting selection and inspection prior to laser-cutting.

particular car within a guaranteed period; and Rolls-Royce Motor Cars can more easily keep tight control on the quality of its service to its customers. Nevertheless, the logistics hub does not stock every single component that goes into building a Phantom. Those replacements that are rarely called for will be dispatched directly from the Goodwood manufacturing plant.

Bearing in mind the fact that the spaceframe construction of the Phantom will, in future, allow other versions of the car to be built in small batches on the same production line, the stores area is easily large enough to cope with most anticipated extra demands for parts. There is a long way to go until the current movement of seven trucks per day rise to that environmentally-imposed limit of twenty.

The whole subject of logistics, even in a Rolls-Royce context, is necessarily methodical – some might even say dull. But that would be to downplay its importance in the resurgence of Rolls-Royce Motor Cars. The geographic, transportation and handling issues that must be considered in Phantom manufacture are worldwide, and the quality of every single component involved must be to Rolls-Royce standards – which means only the very best. Any small failure in this complex process would result in cars remaining unfinished or dealership service falling below par, and that would only tarnish the name of the new Rolls-Royce Phantom.

Holger Groitzsch explains one last logistical problem. "Logistics includes the deliveries of the completed cars, by truck, ship or aircraft. Given the nature of the product, the third option is quite frequently the most efficient, as the delivery time to the customer is reduced considerably. Time saved here, allows longer for us to react to the customers wishes during the build of the car. Delivery by aircraft also solves the problem of controlling a single precious item on its journey to the world's most distant locations. In the end, logistics is really all about serving our customers."

Top: each and every part in its place, ready for locating by computer.

Right: exhaust systems, freshly delivered, being taken to the stores area.

14 TESTING, TESTING...

A theory can be proved by experiment, but no path leads from experiment to the birth of a theory – ALBERT EINSTEIN

Opposite, clockwise from top left: the local wildlife is unimpressed by Rolls-Royce engineering; although unlikely to grace any Christmas card, the test car performs admirably in the snow; P21 rushes towards the midnight sun on a frozen lake in Finland; the 'rooster tail' shows the speed as a test car exhibits its cornering capabilities on slippery surfaces.

A time-consuming part of any new car's development programme, once any computer-aided simulations have been completed, is the testing of real components and prototypes. Theo Martin was, and still is, the engineer responsible for vehicle integration concerning the Rolls-Royce Phantom. He made possible the pre-production testing of the car in the remarkably short time of 34 months.

Followed by 'functional', 'fatigue' and 'endurance' testing, first came 'concept evaluation', which concerned packaging, ergonomic and design evaluation. For these, a vehicle was built which had RR01's basic dimensions, even though the final shape had not yet been agreed. The purpose of this 'car' was to check the configuration of elements and the resulting visibility for driver and passengers. It was fitted with a conventional, front-hinged rear door on one side and a coach door on the other. The vehicle was called Package Ergonomic Design 1 (PED1); it was running by April 2000 but, of course, was never designed for road use.

Concurrently with PED1, laboratory tests were conducted on 'integrated functions' such as aerodynamics, acoustics, heat dissipation and vehicle safety. Meanwhile, the engine and gearbox engineers were under pressure to ready their units for the drivetrain tests on the first roadworthy cars, codenamed KEX (for Komponent Experimental) and IEX (Integration Experimental).

The most important and extensive process was 'functional testing', because it concerns the car as a whole. Components, having performed satisfactorily on test-rigs, were installed in cars where tests were repeated time and again under every condition a customer might impose on their Phantoms.

'Functional testing' was split into four, the first using KEX cars. Two KEX cars were included, one a heavily-modified BMW 7 Series saloon disguising a full Phantom drivetrain, the other the first example of a complete Phantom utilising the spaceframe structure and early versions of the final car's suspension and drivetrain. There were no internal or external trim items, but the cars were fully roadworthy, and evaluated on proving grounds, normal roads and autobahns. This 'Phantom' was camouflaged as a two-door coupe – a fact that many a scoop-motivated magazine editor would have cause to regret as the actual car became, of course, a four-door saloon.

The second stage of functional testing started with the roll-out of PED2, dissimilar to PED1 in as much as it was a roadworthy car. It was fitted with the first interior and exterior trim items. In this form, it was considered to be good enough to allow BMW board members to take a drive.

By mid 2001, crash-testing was underway on complete cars, following computer simulations and

M LT 4090

Above: Tim Leverton and Karl Baumer wait for a ride to work.

Clockwise from top left: lower round headlights twinkle as test car number I06 remains on track under heavy braking; number P21 undergoes acceleration, braking and swerving tests; cold-start and engine temperature evaluations are carried out in Finland's sub-zero temperatures; P21 makes a return run; falling snow on ice does not disturb the Phantom; the test team return to their lodgings, where analysis of the day's testing continues into the 'sunny' night.

individual parts tests. Six 'product process' prototypes and five pre-production cars were used for this. These crash tests confirmed the excellent results engineers had already predicted after computer-simulated events. Still, as Theo Martin recalls, the development team had a collective sigh of relief, as no one yet had practical experience of such a large spaceframe body.

The penultimate stage involved the IEX cars, which became available in February 2001. These 10 vehicles were used for the testing of all the Phantom's functions, and were conducted by eight teams of engineers, in all road, weather and country conditions around the world. Winter testing was carried out in the Alps, Scandinavia and Alaska. The cars were fitted with data-logging equipment and up to 100 measuring locations, mostly for temperature. Martin, however, makes the point that the most important feedback comes from the testers themselves. In the case of the Scandinavian tests, cars were actually driven from Munich to Finland, this 'delivery' drive itself being a great opportunity to make assessments.

Once in the ice and snow, note was taken of the car's heat distribution, demisting capability and general cabin comfort in terms of temperature and humidity. Theo Martin states, "Here the capability of the whole concept shows up immediately. If the basic layout of the vehicle is wrong, none of the electronic helpers can cure the situation. This was the really big showdown, when we tested the Phantom there for the first time. With the conventional type of drivetrain layout, an unloaded axle weight distribution of 50/50, the long wheelbase, the wide track, the immense tyres with their great load ratios, and the relatively sensitive steering, the Phantom performed absolutely brilliantly. The straight running capability was excellent; nevertheless, the response to steering movements had to be of exactly the right degree. The DSC (Dynamic Stability Control) is rarely used but can help with braking on either side, while negating the need to cut power. It is a big asset. Disable the DSC and controlled power drifts are possible with recovery to the straight-ahead position from unbelievable sideways angles."

There is a test to simulate the build-up of snow by driving behind a large truck spraying fresh snow behind it. The test car's air intake manifold or radiator may become snowbound; but not on the Phantom. After 30 minutes behind the truck, there was no loss of performance or engine cooling. The success of this particular test seems to have been due mainly to the Phantom having its air-filter system to the rear of the engine compartment – warm and out of the reach of the snow spray. A secondary benefit of the air-filter position is that quite deep water can be traversed, more so even than with some off-road vehicles if the Phantom's ability to rise one inch on its suspension is utilised. In many countries, snowchains are not only desirable but a legal requirement. Using these, the Phantom performed with the best ratings possible: perfect straight running, very good and predictable cornering, and excellent traction.

Theo Martin has the last word in the snow. "You may realise that I get a little bit carried away regarding the result of these tests, but I am still so excited by

the capabilities of such a large saloon under these conditions. It is a pity only a very few customers will have a chance to experience some of its possibilities during winter driving."

Of course, the other end of the climatic spectrum must also be addressed, and hot-climate testing was carried out in Europe, the USA, South Africa and in the United Arab Emirates. The main objectives were to assess the air-conditioning system, and the thermal efficiency and heat dissipation capabilities of the drivetrain, as well as monitoring all other heat-critical components. A typical test would have been to park the car in the midday sun for an hour or two, until the interior temperature rose sharply. The test team would then enter the car, start it and drive off immediately at the same time as switching on the climate control. The 'cool down' rate was measured and objective evaluations made. Results were excellent, especially in the rear of the car, where the large 'C' pillars reduced the sun's direct rays and separate outlets for each passenger place distributed cooling air more evenly. The engine underwent thermal efficiency tests at idle and high speed, city driving and at high altitude. No problems were encountered, even when the Phantom was subjected to dust ingress tests for both the cabin and engine air intake system.

The final stage of functional testing began when the first Product Process Prototypes (PPP) were ready in December 2001. The addition of 20 of these cars to the testing fleet improved availability for the testers, but time was now pressing. As with IEX, the PPPs were

A much warmer climate than Finland! Test car number I01 is studied during hot climate testing in these pictures, on the roads and deserts of Dubai.

Top and right: no doubt the cityscape of Tokyo will be home to production Phantoms. Meanwhile, a lightly disguised test car enjoys the cut and thrust of the ancient, narrow streets.

Clockwise from top left: the car is wired to computers: not a pretty sight but the mass of information gained was invaluable; where do I start? An engineer downloads information for analysis; not a balloon – hot weather testing completed, 101 returns to the docks of Dubai; 101 sports an engine revolution counter to aid drivers in test cycles – note outside temperature gauge.

also placed in the endurance testing programme. A particularly nasty functional test was the DyKo (Dynamic Korrosion test). A pre-production car was subjected to stone chipping and scratches on the bodywork. The car was then alternately left in an accelerated salt-spray chamber and driven through a salt spray tunnel at 50mph for two days. This two day cycle is repeated 50 times. The severity of the tests was equal to the potential salt corrosion a car might expect to encounter over 10 to 50 years, depending on the individual components. When the test was completed, the entire body was dismantled including opening up of the body sections. The results were such that the all-aluminium body was absolutely perfect. As Theo Martin says: "We are quite sure that any Phantoms used in a normal way will outlast any member of our engineering team." And none of them are septuagenarians!

'Fatigue' testing in the laboratories had been running since the start of the test programme. Early results using the first real KEX Phantom showed that further work was necessary, and this continued in parallel on both cars and test-rigs. A 'normal duty' cycle was developed in which 6,200 miles on the road-simulating test-rig equated to 186,000 miles on the actual road. A 'special incidences' cycle catered for events estimated to occur no more than 100 times in a

Above: a German-registered pre-production car is piloted along an autobahn. The front and rear covers discourage press photographers from snapping rogue shots.

Above right: P22 returning from high-altitude testing on Mount Fuji.

Right: Japanese test car undergoes the 'water test'; repeated splashes at varying speeds show up any water ingress to the mechanical systems and the car's interior.

Top left: Dubai wildlife notices the Phantom.

Top right: the camels are intrigued.

Right: a closer inspection is necessary.

Opposite: What was that masked car?

Top left: replacement air springs and shock absorbers about to be installed after a fast desert run.

Top right: engineers enjoy a refuelling stop on a wet and windy day.

Below: an engineer analyses test data before setting up for the next run.

car's normal life; for example, high-speed U-turns or extremely heavy braking while driving over a railway level-crossing. Once-in-a-lifetime events, such as driving a fully-laden car over a 170mm-high kerb were assessed in a 'mis-use' cycle!

'Endurance' testing was undertaken on PPPs, in parallel with the functional tests. This was time-consuming, and so these tests were mostly covered in two shifts, and occasionally with three shifts, on a continuous basis. The cars were virtually production-level-models. The tests themselves were performed at BMW's proving grounds in Miramas, in the south of France, and on designated road runs in Germany, Great Britain and in the USA. The amount of city driving was relatively high, to reflect the probable use customers would make of their cars.

The nature of a largely hand-built, low-production process, however, helped speed up the programme. Results were acted upon with much greater speed than is the case for mass-produced cars. By cramming in such a great deal of testing, using a relatively small number of cars, the entire test programme was condensed to a much shorter time frame than that generally expected in the car industry. It was yet another demonstration of the extraordinary way the Phantom had come together.

Top left: about to test cross wind stability on a Japanese bridge.

Top right: P22 has a change of driver in the unusual setting of a Japanese paddy field.

Right: fast cornering is handled beautifully. See the offside front tyre to judge the stresses with which the car is coping.

15 THE WORLD GREETS THE PHANTOM

To build, in all, not the most luxurious car in the world, but the most perfect – remembering that perfection respects all details, and ignores not one – ROLLS-ROYCE ADVERTISEMENT FROM 1926

Opposite: selected members of the world's press are introduced to the Phantom in Santa Barbara, California.

If Rolls-Royce had one significant problem to deal with when launching the Phantom, it was that publicity had simply not been possible.

The original, complex agreement with Volkswagen specifically excluded any press releases, publicity or use of the Rolls-Royce trademarks before 1 January 2003. Under normal motor industry circumstances, a build-up to the car's official unveiling would have been undertaken, possibly including such attention-getting techniques as sneak previews, tantalising advertisements, and 'leaks' of information to favoured media.

Unusually, the car would be in showrooms ready for purchase on the very day it was released to the world. The company had two fantastic showpieces to trumpet on that winter day in 2003: a brand new car and a brand new manufacturing plant and head office. But everyone at Rolls-Royce who had been working hard on the project for up to five years (a relatively short timescale from clean sheet of paper to production) was still anxious about the reaction of an expectant world.

During the pre-production phase, the car had been shown to carefully chosen individuals in 'closed room' presentations across the world. These were static displays of the car and specific features such as rear seating layouts. All the participants were potential customers and representatives of possible dealerships, and they were all sworn to secrecy. Senior designers and engineers were always present so that any questions or comments could be addressed at the highest level. The 'closed rooms' were located in major cities such as London, Munich, Hong Kong and Tokyo. Venues across the United States were also included. In the Middle East, cultural differences demanded that the Phantom was taken on a tour of the palace homes of respected VIPs. The 'closed room' sessions were later expanded to include selected and trustworthy members of the press, who were invited to Goodwood. There, they saw the final production version, and were allowed interviews and even photographs, all under strict embargo. Graham Biggs, Rolls-Royce corporate communications manager takes up the story. "Having given the press access to information on the car under embargo, we managed a 'big bang' impact on 3 January. The results were very pleasing. We made a lot of front covers on important magazines." To coincide with the lifting of the embargo, a major press day was arranged at the manufacturing plant.

Biggs continues: "We had around 160 journalists from all over the world, carefully selected to be representative of the more important, high quality media. An open invitation to the world's press could have resulted in several thousand of them turning up, which would not have allowed a serious inspection of the car for anyone. We started the day by giving them lunch at Goodwood House. They were then taken to the

Above: the unimportant looking and run down exterior of this 'closed room' helped to conceal the secrets within.

Top left: a Phantom awaits the start of a 'closed room' presentation to potential customers.

Top right: a 'closed room' participant's first sight of the Phantom Rolls-Royce.

back of the plant, entering a specially constructed doorway, which led through a darkened tunnel to a temporary presentation theatre. Unbeknown to the journalists, the theatre was inside the production hall. An unveiling of the car was made inside the theatre. The sound and light show continued as two sides of the theatre were dropped to reveal the inside of the manufacturing plant and the production line. It was quite dramatic, with enormous visual impact."

The event was a huge success; the 10 selected TV crews with their satellite uplink trucks and the radio journalists spread the word immediately, while those who supplied the written word hurried off to make their deadlines. The day provided a springboard from which to build future press coverage. There was no time to rest on laurels. Two days later the presentation team had to be at the North American International Auto Show in Detroit.

The Goodwood unveiling did not detract from the US presentation, which was in two parts. The Phantom was revealed at a separate, BMW-hosted function, away from the main event, the night before its grand entrance on the show stand. The Phantom had arrived, its tripartite launch having a hugely positive response throughout the world.

Everyone in the media had the chance to see the car, to sit in it and walk around it. Next was the opportunity for the chosen few to drive it. Shortly after the Detroit motor show, at the beginning of February, 100 journalists and certain other interested parties were taken to Santa Barbara in California. The base was the Bacara Resort & Spa. A route had been devised, heading north towards San Francisco, which took in freeways as well as mountains and country roads. A lunch stop was arranged at a vineyard, followed by a journey along Route 1 and the stunningly beautiful coastal road back into Santa Barbara. The whole essence of the driving day was not to say "Look, this is the best car in the world"; instead, it was to allow the reporters to make up their own minds as to how good the car really was. Graham Biggs was exhausted but immensely pleased when the launch was completed, because he had compressed the conventional motor industry introduction of a new car into just six weeks. Interestingly, one of Britain's most popular motoring journalists had been banned a few years earlier from the Rolls-Royce factory at Crewe, because of his derisory and negative comments about the cars. He was now not only effusive in his praise of the Phantom, but he also voted it his car of the year.

On the morning of Saturday, 10 May, company chairman Tony Gott was a worried man. His concern was not about the success of the Phantom, as the world's press had already received it with acclaim. His apprehension was due to the fact that the grand opening

Above: chairman Tony Gott welcomes representatives of the company's proposed dealership in Bahrain, to a Munich 'closed room' presentation.

Right: the Detroit motor show car awaits admiration.

of the manufacturing plant and head office, together with the public introduction of the car, was taking place that very evening.

This was an extravaganza superior even to the press launch earlier in the year. Gott naturally wanted everything to be to a Rolls-Royce standard and, by once again staging the event inside the manufacturing plant and head office, with specific and ingenious alterations for the evening, he was making sure it would be unforgettable.

Each and every guest was greeted by the chairman and his fellow directors, as they assembled in a welcoming area within the head office building; historic Rolls-Royce artifacts had been assembled, dating from the company's earliest days to the present. Perhaps the article holding most fascination for the guests was Royce's own drawing board, kindly loaned by the Sir Henry Royce Memorial Foundation. Many found it impossible not to touch, perhaps for good luck or maybe in the hope that 'greatness' may be catching!

Guests could then make their way to a specially created reception area at the end of the production line, for a glass of champagne. From there they could make a tour of the facility; starting at the arrival point of the spaceframes from Dingolfing, continuing through the surface finishing centre, along the production line, leather and wood workshops, the finishing and testing areas, and culminating beside a completed car 'shrink-wrapped' in its protective coating, ready for shipping. At specific places of interest, experts were available to answer questions.

Dinner followed in a newly created auditorium, where the excellent meal was enhanced by the music of the Royal Philharmonic Concert Orchestra. While the olfactory and auditory senses were sated, the sense of sight was treated to displays by the Ballet Rambert Dance Company, Mongolian contortionists from the Cirque de Soleil, and the Mazeppa Ukrainian Cossack Dancers. Each performance was introduced by short film presentations demonstrating aspects of the Phantom, of which the artistes were illustrative. The entertainment concluded with a film entitled 'The Journey to Goodwood', which

Studio shot that demonstrates the presence of the Phantom.

showed, in storyboard form, the philosophy, motivation, design and manufacture of the Phantom, along with the building of the Goodwood facility.

Tony Gott made a welcoming speech in which, with the very clever use of modern technology, he appeared to have a conversation with the image of Sir Henry Royce displayed on the giant video screen behind. 'Sir Henry' asked if the Phantom was a suitable car to carry his name and Tony Gott explained why indeed it was! The real-life guest of honour, however, was The Lord Montagu of Beaulieu. In his speech he referred to the fact that his father, John Montagu, had officially opened the Rolls-Royce factory at Derby in July 1908. On that occasion, John Montagu had symbolically switched on the factory's electricity supply; 95 years later, Edward Montagu made do with arriving in his father's 1910 Silver Ghost, and making a fine speech.

It has long been a Rolls-Royce Motor Cars tradition, within the factories, that the completion of the first example of a new model is celebrated by the entire workforce banging spanners on resonant surfaces, such as parts bins or metal benches. The Goodwood manufacturing plant continued the ritual, when all the guests (they had been given small, chrome-plated spanners for the purpose) 'hammered out' the first Goodwood Phantom.

The evening concluded with dancing. Tony Gott need not have been concerned; his team had done everything expected of them. The event was a huge success in itself, for the Goodwood plant, and most importantly, for the Phantom.

Meanwhile, sales and marketing director Howard Mosher had been overseeing the establishment of a new worldwide dealer network. All former Rolls-Royce dealerships were considered, as well as a carefully chosen selection of dealerships attached to other prestige car manufacturers. Those who could meet the stringent standards set by Project Rolls-Royce were offered contracts. The dealer network, like the press launch, is of crucial importance to the success of a car such as the Phantom. With an annual production rate of 1000 cars, mass-market advertising, such as television commercials and newspapers advertisements, would not be cost-effective. An important aid to sales for a car such as the Phantom is old-fashioned word of mouth recommendations from owners to prospective customers. So how these potential buyers are received and catered to by dealers is of paramount importance.

Look carefully at the door edge and the umbrella housing can be seen.

No acned youths with white socks and black shoes or overweight chain smokers furtively hiding brown bag lunches here – no requests to "call in next week, we might have some brochures by then", or "It's the Rolls salesman's day off". Sales staff, indeed everyone who works at a Rolls-Royce dealership, needed to be highly-trained and very knowledgeable about the cars. After all, possible owners will be entering a relationship with the dealer staff for the entire time they own the car. No Rolls-Royce salesperson wants to sell a customer one car – he or she wants to supply that person over a lifetime of Rolls-Royce ownership. So the service offered has to entirely match the car's standards of design and engineering. Chairman Tony Gott explains the Rolls-Royce ethos: "The Rolls-Royce market is a special market, access is by personal relationship. It is also helped by the fact that everyone wants Rolls-Royce to succeed; nobody wants a world without Rolls-Royce. For a customer, it is important that someone can explain the heritage, the design and the engineering content of

A beautiful setting embellishes the stylish curves of the Phantom – here seen at the Villa d'Este, Italy.

Tony Gott, chairman and CEO of Rolls-Royce Motor Cars Ltd., speaking at the official opening of the Goodwood manufacturing plant and the head office.

REACTION FROM JOHN BLATCHLEY

Rolls-Royce would have been very different without John Blatchley. As designer of the 1946 Silver Dawn, 1955 Silver Cloud and 1966 Silver Shadow, his styling skills shaped the cars for almost 40 years. After taking early retirement in 1969, he became a virtual recluse, and turned his back on the car world.

Finally, however, the 89-year old Blatchley was honoured with an award acknowledging his contribution to the marque. He was presented with the Sir Henry Royce Memorial Foundation's 'Pursuit of Excellence' trophy in a ceremony at the Rolls-Royce Enthusiasts' Club headquarters in Northampton in May 2003.

While many Rolls-Royce traditionalists professed to find the Phantom too radical a departure for their tastes, Blatchley – the real creator of Rolls-Royce's late-20th century image – likes it.

"I'm a fan of the Phantom," he says. "BMW came to see me three years ago and showed me their possible designs. There was literally only one I thought was any good, and it's the one they've built. I think they've done a marvellous job."

the car. It's really not appropriate to just say 'here's the car, it costs this amount of money, now please buy it!' We need to explain why it is so special, but not in flowery marketing terms. We cannot rely on providing blanket generic information as the mainstream carmakers do. We know where the major markets are for our cars, so we select the best, most knowledgeable, most 'aware' dealers in town. In fact, it has been a very competitive situation for the dealers and there was no shortage of applicants for our franchise. We looked at their business plans and their expertise and made a decision based on our judgment of their abilities."

In the United States, the dealerships are nearly all previously established Rolls-Royce dealers. In the United Kingdom, about half are new franchises, and in the Middle East they are all new appointees – it seems this last area has a plethora of suitable candidates, so Rolls-Royce was truly able to pick and choose.

Howard Mosher, who began his life in the automobile industry at American Motors, spent time at Rolls-Royce Motors, Crewe, and Land Rover, before becoming head of sales and marketing for Rolls-Royce at Goodwood. During his time at Land Rover he undertook the task of advising Karl Baumer, then analysing the viability of Project Rolls-Royce in its entirety. Mosher and Baumer realised it was more important for a putative dealership to have a passion for selling Rolls-Royce cars than to have a large turnover of other brands. An intimate knowledge of customers' lifestyles and motoring needs was very important, and the ability to handle every customer in a comfortable and individual way.

Dealerships may well handle other brands, Mosher concluded, but a dedicated showroom area and a specific Rolls-Royce salesperson were essential. A complete knowledge of new and used cars, along with spare parts and servicing requirements would be needed; also, a willingness to take cars in part-exchange. For the company's part, it would recognise that too many dealerships too close together would impede the earning potential of any one, a problem that had existed in the past.

A dealership, old or new, has to have a dedicated sales area, with room enough to display the Phantom to its best advantage. A backdrop using the corporate colour scheme of verona and chamois (the colours of plums and clotted cream respectively!) is insisted upon, and a suitably furnished seating area within which

Lord Montagu arrives at the opening ceremony for the Goodwood manufacturing plant, being driven in his father's 1910 Silver Ghost.

colours and trim may be selected is also a prerequisite. The samples of paint colours, available leather and wood finishes are displayed on specially constructed trays, which are manufactured to Rolls-Royce standards. Even their storage cabinet is actually a piece of furniture of the finest quality.

Should a customer want to discuss the purchase of his or her new car at the Goodwood manufacturing plant, there are a choice of three rooms set aside in which to do so. One is a modern room with a hint of sleek 1960s styling to it; the second adopts an exotic 'Scandinavian-style' aura, with furniture in bright primary colours; and the third is the more 'clubby' option, a boardroom with the accent on medium-toned natural woods together with an English country house setting featuring red leather furniture and darker woodwork. The latter clever mixture of traditional elements is a particularly natural setting for the Phantom.

Another useful tool in the successful marketing of the Phantom is the product brochure. At a time when many manufacturers have rejected the high-quality sales brochure – often leaving customers to use the internet to find the detailed information they want – Rolls-Royce has produced a pair of A4 sized booklets worthy of the car.

The first booklet contains sketches supported by text that refers more to concepts and ideals than plain hard facts. Then it presents high quality photographs of various key elements of the car, demonstrating the virtues that have rapidly become synonymous with the Phantom – authority, functionality, quality and excellence of design. The second booklet reveals the finish options and technical information. Beautifully produced, these booklets might well be the first point of contact between company and customer.

REACTIONS FROM THE MOTORING MEDIA

AUTOCAR MAGAZINE, JANUARY 2003 – BY EDITOR IN CHIEF STEVE CROPLEY

'The Rolls absorbs it all in silence. There are no bumps.'

CAR MAGAZINE, FEBRUARY 2003

'A confident revival of a grand old name...
Step behind the wheel of the Phantom and you know this is a car like no other. There is nothing like it. Nothing.'

CAR MAGAZINE, MAY 2003

'The Rolls-Royce delivers the greatest luxury and refinement and the most truly special driving experience.'

CAR MAGAZINE, MAY 2003 – BY DESIGN CRITIC AND COLUMNIST STEPHEN BAYLEY

'The Rolls-Royce is a horribly boastful car, although others would say it is an 'imposing' one. The proportions have been handled well (after a lot of diligent study of the carriage trade), but the total effect is one of coloratura swagger which might suit a rapper, but would not suit someone who could tell his Titian from his Tiepolo.'

CAR MAGAZINE, MAY 2003 – BY EUROPEAN EDITOR GEORG KACHER

'The Rolls Royce is overtly pompous, ornate, aggressively prestigious. And so it should be, for the R-R brand image is not open to interpretation. The big question is: are there enough rich people prepared to splash out on such a polarising automobile, especially in times like these?'

CAR & DRIVER MAGAZINE, MAY 2003

'Call it tradition made modern.'

EVO MAGAZINE, MARCH 2003 – BY JOHN SIMISTER

'It rides as a Rolls-Royce should, yet steers better than a Bentley Arnage Red Label...The engine finally reveals its cultured, upper class tones, squirting the motor car forward...This is a ridiculous car by normal, sane standards. But it's beautifully-created, full of personality, entirely at ease with itself.'

BBC TOP GEAR MAGAZINE, NOVEMBER 2003

'In the Rolls there is a sense of light, airy and uncluttered space boldly trimmed with innovative materials and designs...The Rolls-Royce indulges the greatest luxury known to humankind, that of not really needing to achieve anything.'

REACTIONS FROM THE WIDER MEDIA

THE DAILY TELEGRAPH, FEBRUARY 2003 – BY MOTORING CORRESPONDENT ANDREW ENGLISH

'The Phantom offers a charming, laid-back approach to driving.'

THE DAILY TELEGRAPH, MARCH 2003 – BY JASON BARLOW

'The Phantom has atmosphere, ambience and attitude. It can also be driven with what aristocratic types might call verve.'

COUNTRY LIFE MAGAZINE, MARCH 2003 – BY MOTORING CORRESPONDENT JAMES MAY

'Two days of driving the Phantom had me thinking that other luxury cars are missing the point...The new Rolls-Royce is big, powerful and expensive, yet charming and somehow polite.'

THE ORIENT EXPRESS MAGAZINE, MAY 2003 – BY SIR STIRLING MOSS

'Such cars stand or fall by their ability to provide world-beating ride and refinement and, in my experience, the Phantom ranks with the finest... The Phantom is a great car but, more importantly, it is a great Rolls-Royce.'

THE SYDNEY MORNING HERALD, JUNE 2003 – BY TONY DAVIS

'The interior is opulent beyond measure, hiding myriad comfort, convenience, and safety technology behind fields of leather, wood, cashmere and brushed aluminium.'

THE FINANCIAL TIMES, MARCH 2003 – BY MOTORING CORRESPONDENT MICHAEL HARVEY

'The rear pew in the Phantom is cosy. Intimate. Sexy even.'

REACTIONS FROM ENTHUSIASTS

FROM ROWAN ATKINSON, WRITING IN *OCTANE* MAGAZINE, JUNE 2003

'The exterior design has been widely questioned but the overall effect is undeniably grand, to the extent that I think prospective owners will have to be rather confident, happy people. Those racked with self-doubt need not apply. If they do take the plunge they will be driving a car very different from anything else on the road. I liked it a lot. This is a car devoted to easing and soothing and pampering so that a journey in it is simply made as effortless as possible.'

FROM LORD MONTAGU OF BEAULIEU, WHO OFFICIALLY OPENED THE GOODWOOD PLANT IN MAY 2003

'In my opinion, Rolls-Royce has created a car well in the spirit of the pre- and post-war models and, although it could be said that the new Phantom is 'squarer' than some people anticipated, it is nevertheless magnificently fitted out with every modern gadget and comfort that could be imagined...As we all get used to the shape, I am convinced it will fit in well with its ancestors, illustrating the century-old prestige of Rolls-Royce as being 'The Best Car in the World'.'

FROM JOHN DONNER, PROMINENT ROLLS-ROYCE COLLECTOR

'I got in it to hate it. I looked at it to hate it. I was only in it for five minutes when I became its best ambassador. It is the most amazing car and it will become one of the great Rolls-Royces, the Silver Ghost of the 21st century.'

16 A TANTALISING GLIMPSE OF FANTASY

The woods are lovely, dark and deep
But I have promises to keep
And miles to go before I sleep
And miles to go before I sleep

– ROBERT FROST

Opposite: Marek Djordjevic's early sketches for the experimental 100EX show definitive links to open-top Rolls-Royce cars of the past.

On 13 January 2004, the employees of Rolls-Royce Motor Cars gathered around the end of the production line to celebrate the completion of the 500th Phantom. It had been only 377 days since the first customer's car was ready for delivery and now, as it enters the second year of production, the company is well placed to meet its target of five cars per day, which equates to an annual production of 1000 cars.

Despite recent political tensions between certain elements of East and West, the winds of the luxury car trade are set fair. The world demand for luxurious and super high-performance cars is widely thought by car industry watchers to be about 5,000 units annually. The 1,000 cars per annum target that Rolls-Royce Motor Cars is on track to achieve therefore represents 20 per cent of the market. Subdivide that market into cars in direct competition with the Phantom and, at the time of writing, it has already achieved sales of over 50 per cent of this exalted sector. The Phantom has a model life expectancy of 10 to 12 years, during which time changes can be expected, as improvements become possible and new legislation demands ever more stringent requirements.

Tony Gott, chairman and CEO of Rolls-Royce Motor Cars Ltd., emphasises that the Phantom will remain the mainstay of Rolls-Royce production in the immediate future. It has been designed without compromise to its present form, but the structural elements within its spaceframe allow alterations with a degree of ease and fiscal prudence, which is something other monocoque or separate-chassis cars really cannot match.

Of course, many potential Rolls-Royce owners will want exactly what the Phantom provides. After all, the car's designers took a great deal of notice, in the 'closed room' market research presentations to dealers and clients, of what was required of the car. However, Rolls-Royce has, since its earliest days, been able to supply an open car and the new custodians of the marque recognise this fact.

At the Geneva motor show on Tuesday, 2 March 2004, Rolls-Royce unveiled an experimental car – 100EX, produced as part of the company's centenary celebrations. Using an adaptation of the Phantom's spaceframe structure, the car has a wheelbase four inches shorter. It is a two-door, full four-seater convertible with fully disappearing hood and many exciting features. Its present identity follows Rolls-Royce practice since 1919 of giving its large horsepower experimental cars an 'EX' suffix and a series number. In this case, 100 was chosen to represent the anniversary.

Tony Gott was adamant that the design of 100EX should comply with several criteria. The most important were that – in spite of being purely a showpiece – it would emphasise the vision, the competence and the

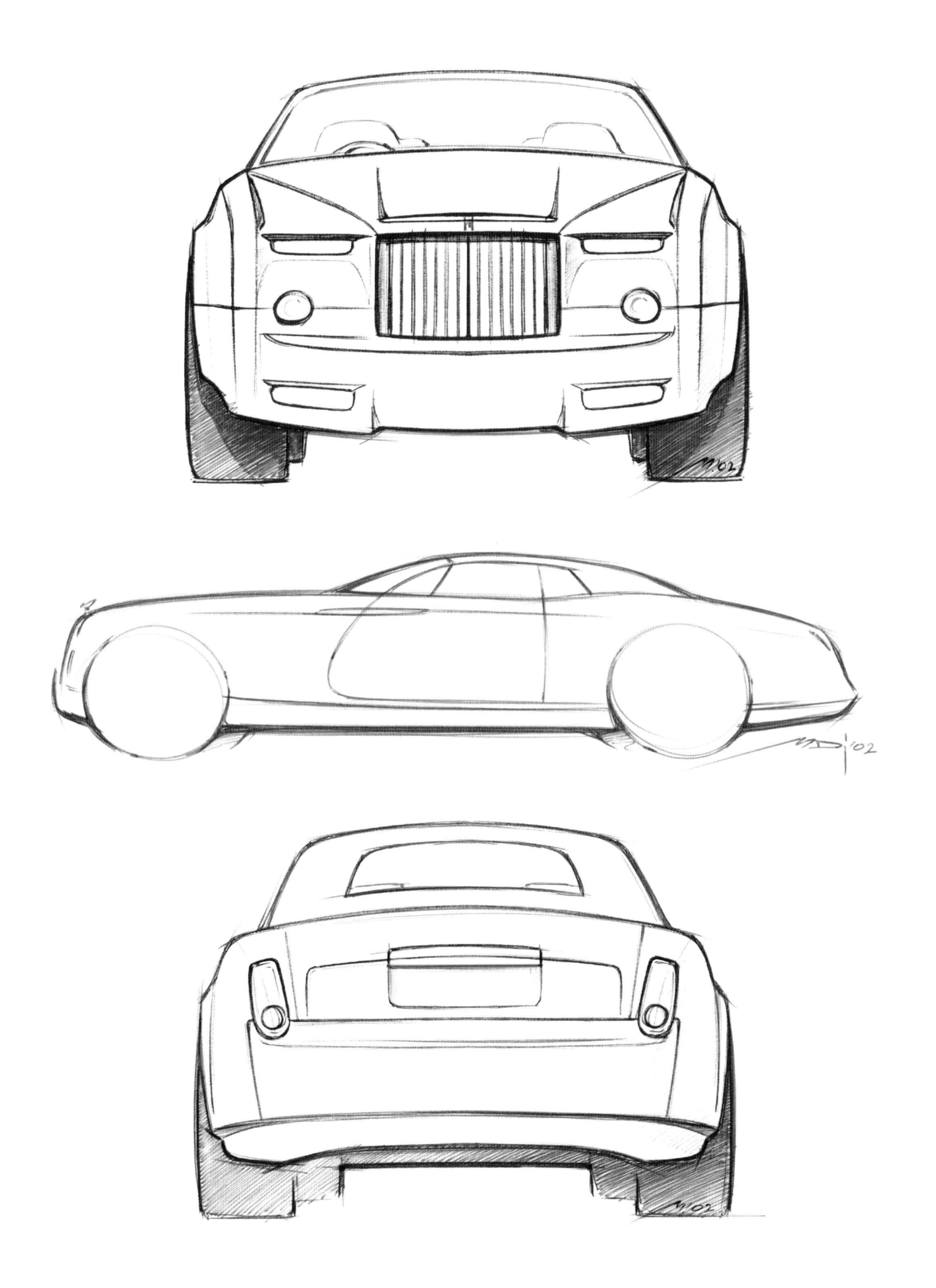

100EX, 'one-off' experimental drophead coupe.

engineering skills of the new Rolls-Royce company. The flight of fancy, if you will, that celebrates the 100 years of the marque.

The exterior was sculpted by the Phantom's exterior designer Marek Djordjevic, at the Designworks Studio in California. Much of his inspiration came from the same state – it is a natural backdrop for such a car. Southern California is also the home of several outstanding motor museums and private car collections where benchmark comparisons could be made with great, magnificently-bodied cars from the 1920s and 1930s. Ian Cameron is clear in his mind that these fantastic – in the true sense of the word – cars from previous ages were used as inspiration only for the designers of 100EX. The car is as extravagant and bold in its conception as the pre-war icons but, just as they were the cars of their day, so 100EX is, if not a car of our time, then a car of our near future.

Meanwhile, in Europe, Adolf Fischer, the development engineer for the Phantom's engine, was busy arranging for the centrepiece feature of 100EX: an experimental V16 engine. This he achieved by taking the Phantom's basic V12 components and adding four extra cylinders. So 100EX is powered by an engine which is equally as exotic and imposing as the car's coachwork. In its present state of development, given this is an experimental car only, and therefore a test bed for ongoing development, the V16 is less complex than the Phantom's fully-certified production V12. The V16 engine runs sweetly and silently, a blip of the throttle

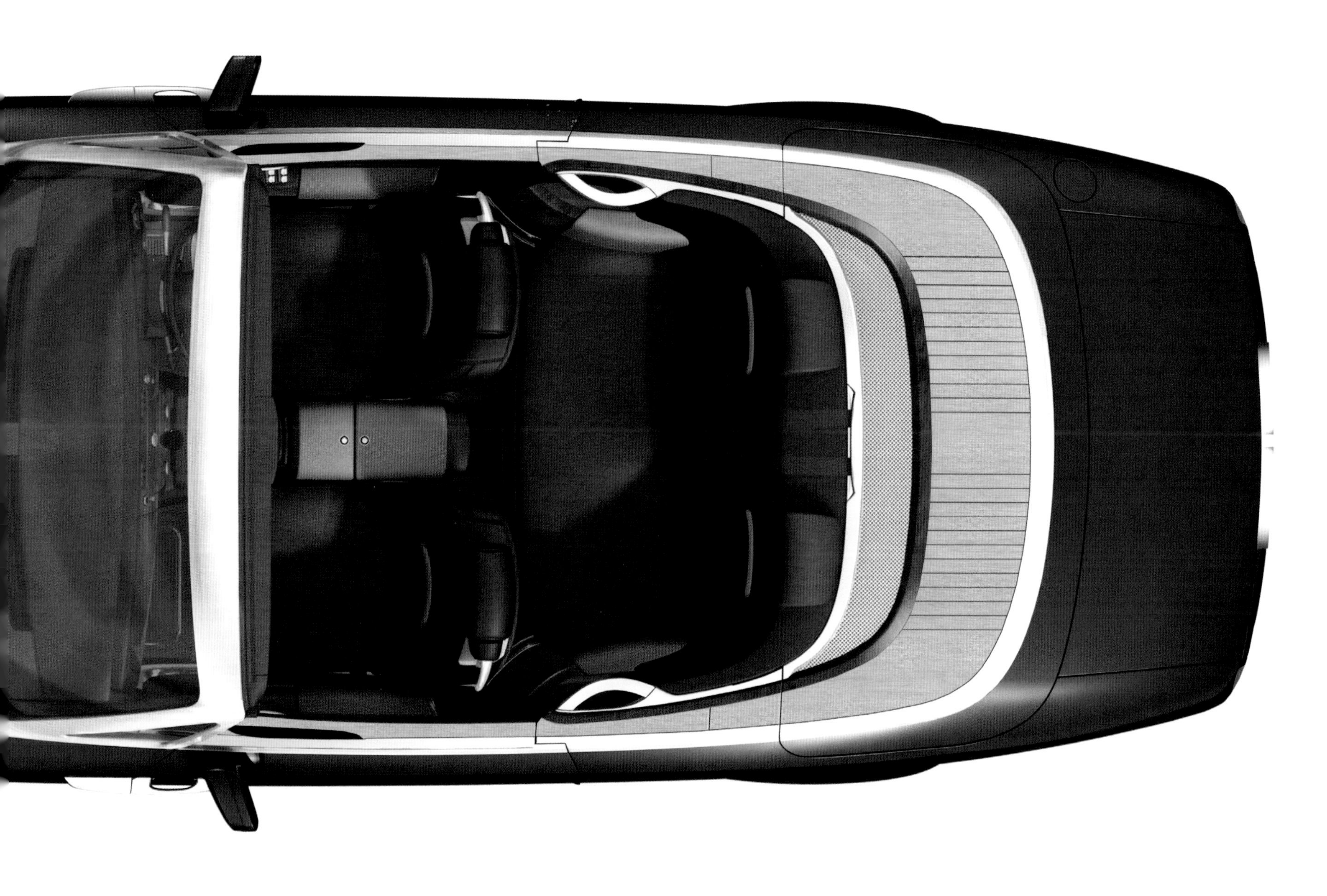

Very little room is lost to the hood mechanism for rear seat passengers. Also, note the look of strength imparted by the 'machined from solid' windscreen frame.

producing a muffled roar which, even with the bonnet raised, is but a refined and exciting hint of the power produced. The old trick of balancing a penny on the radiator top is now performed with a one Euro coin!

Ian Cameron admits he considered creating a straightforward Phantom convertible for the Geneva exhibit. It might have made quite an acceptable concept car, but it would have been nowhere near as uncompromising. Cameron says that he was striving for "lavish sexiness" for 100EX, and a simple adaptation of the Phantom would not have yielded that. The car's spaceframe is nonetheless developed from Phantom technology and the mechanical systems, apart from the engine, are similar to the Phantom's, even down to the imposing wheels.

Coming from the same stable as the Phantom, the car exudes coachbuilt quality and is, of course, large for a car of its type. But, as with all great designs, if seen without a reference with which to gauge its mass, 100EX could be any size at all – only the proximity of other objects betrays its generous scale. From the side, the car has a true voluptuousness enhanced by a slight rise of the waist-high body top as it moves towards the rear, a design trait also seen on the Corniche models since their introduction as an alternative to the four-door Silver Shadow saloon of the early 1970s. The two doors of 100EX are hinged at the rear, recalling the great coachbuilders of the authentic concours d'elegance years of the 1920s and 1930s. They are set well back towards the rear wheel arches, giving easy access for rear seat

A cloth hood was chosen to allow the car's occupants to 'enjoy the gentle patter of raindrops'. It also looks so much better than a metal roof.

passengers. The resulting distance between the front edge of the doors and the front wheel arch gives maximum stylish impact. The curve of the doors' front edge rises towards the top. So does the swage line between the front wheel and door, albeit not so steeply. In line with these, the entire front of the car 'leans' back towards the top, but at less of an angle than the swage and door.

The front lights are subtly different to the Phantom's. They are smaller with the running and headlights set closer together. Naturally, the legendary mascot is proudly retained. Marek Djordjevic explains that he "wished the side view to express the power and speed available, but not in an aggressive, forward-thrusting stance." He wanted to create a sense that 100EX had the power to take the car to its ultimate speed rapidly but in a truly relaxed manner. Another iteration of waftability.

How to incorporate a proper, three-dimensional radiator grille but still aim for a contemporary look? Djordjevic overcame the dilemma by leaning the radiator shell back, merging it a little with the front panels but not allowing any bodywork metal to obscure or supplant the radiator itself. The result is a streamlined but undiminished structure. The space demands of accommodating the V16 engine have meant the radiator header tank has had to be positioned right inside the radiator shell – on early cars, its original 'home', of course, but not seen there in Rolls-Royce cars since the late 1930s.

The bonnet is narrower than the Phantom's. Its sides follow the natural line from radiator shell corners to windscreen sides. The bonnet itself is a work of art, being milled from a single piece of aluminium with a diamond-patterned geodesic strengthening structure underneath to keep this long panel arrow-straight. The windscreen structure is also milled from solid aluminium. It has triangular front quarterlights formed inside the resulting 'A'-shaped frame. Ian Cameron explains that this gives good side visibility without compromising the optical requirements of a windscreen that needed rearward support for rollover crash protection.

With hood down and stowed beneath the marine-styled rear cover, the nautical influence on the interior is evident.

Flying in the face of current trends, it was decided to have a cloth hood rather than the convertible metal top that so many convertibles feature these days. This large item is made of a water-resistant material fabricated from woven wire strands, and lined with a wool/cashmere blend fabric. The designers felt the gentle sound of rain dropping onto fabric would enhance the comfortable environment of the car's interior, rather than the staccato drumming on a metal top!

The space into which the hood stows is unbelievably small, leaving an unencumbered luggage boot whatever the weather. Once stowed, the hood is concealed below a flush panel finished in marine-style bleached teak decking redolent of boat-tailed tourers of the 1920s and the delightful Thames slipper launches still sailing today.

As a last touch of sensible design to enhance any outdoors occasion, the bootlid is split into a top-hinged upper section and a bottom-hinged lower one. When open, the lower lid rests parallel to the ground, forming an ideal picnic table or, at the very least, a support for a decent bottle of champagne in an appropriate iced water container.

Charles Coldham, the Phantom's interior designer, has exhibited his masterful design skills once again for 100EX. Apart from a facia obviously similar to the Phantom, the interior of 100EX design is completely different. Where wood is required, he has used teak and mahogany, which are suitable for a car designed for open-air use. Seats are more curved and supportive and have flat, unfluted facings. Their slimline seatback design means there is still generous access to the back of 100EX despite the car being four inches shorter overall than the Phantom. The large doors have panel trims containing armrests and storage lockers. The stitching for all the leather work is very fine, enhancing the sense of space within the interior.

The rear seat is a further step along the path taken by the Phantom's own 'lounge' seat, in as much as it wraps around more, and is even cosier without seeming at all cramped. This feeling of space is partly due to the fact that the hood mechanism does not drastically reduce

Charles Coldham's final concept sketch has been followed almost to the letter for the completed 100EX.

the seat's width. In fact, there are even substantial vertical storage spaces forward of the seat's edge, equipped as individual left- and right-side cocktail cabinets.

Coldham has drawn heavily from the design well of classic and contemporary boats and yachts for his inspiration. How this amazing designer can create a car's interior that is absolutely contemporary and yet give an almost subliminal impression of nautical influences from another time is bewildering.

At the point where the interior meets the exterior, the cockpit of 100EX features a polished aluminium door capping inlaid with bleached teak. This links the alloy windscreen components to that of the similarly finished, divided surround to the wood decking of the hood cover. The exposed elements of the spaceframe, in the form of the windscreen surround, is a visual reminder of the car's masterful mixture of form and function.

100EX will remain as an experimental test bed for possible engineering and design solutions, as Rolls-Royce does not intend it to evolve into a production car. If it were to do so, in the view of the author, it would be a league above any other convertible currently on offer, and would set rival manufacturers wondering how on earth they could match it.

Above: the experimental car's facia bears a close family resemblance to that of the Phantom. Note the marine-like floor coverings.

Right: the lower of the two boot lids can also act as a table for a sumptuous picnic.

Part 4

ROLLS-ROYCE AND GOODWOOD

17 HOW ROLLS-ROYCE MOTOR CARS CHOSE 'GLORIOUS GOODWOOD'

Give me Goodwood on a summer's day, and you can keep the rest of the world – ROY SALVADORI

Chichester harbour from the air (photo by Stephen Hayward).

Opposite, top: Goodwood House is just one of the local attractions that complement the British essence of Rolls-Royce motor cars.

Opposite, below: Rolls-Royce could find no other location in England with such a great combination of practicality and natural beauty as Goodwood (photo by Mike Caldwell).

Project Rolls-Royce, as the new enterprise had to be known until 1 January, 2003, faced two problems at its inauguration: the design and development of a brand new car, and the design and building of a new manufacturing plant and head office. While the Phantom itself was under close development scrutiny, the buildings presented their own challenge.

It would have been perfectly practical to build a Rolls-Royce at a BMW facility in Germany. In fact, it made logical, economic sense to do that since the engine and bodywork were to be fabricated in Germany anyway. Assembling the car there may possibly have been more cost-effective, but a Rolls-Royce built outside England would have been totally unacceptable to customers. BMW knew that the Phantom had to be much more than just a 'product'.

Rolls-Royce, after all, is one of the most revered names in automotive history and it has always been distinctively English – not British, but English. It is often impossible these days to tell the nationality of most new models because they do not have one. Ford, for example, presents a slightly different face in every market: British buyers are convinced Ford is somehow British, just as German buyers know that Fords are made in Cologne; either way, the Ford car they buy may well be built in Belgium or Spain.

Grand motoring marques, however, have always had a distinct national identity. A Ferrari could not come from any country but Italy, and that is a big part of its appeal. It is like the cuisine of a region: the supermarket replica is rarely a substitute.

The Phantom, therefore, had to hail from England. Since the enterprise was being started from scratch, finding simply the most appropriate location was a great opportunity. An industrial site like Crewe had always been the opposite of what the leaders of Project Rolls-Royce desired: a facility as uplifting and appealing for potential owners as the new car itself was the order of the day. Customers were likely to want to see their cars being built; an environment that enhanced this requirement was needed.

Several locations met Project Rolls-Royce's specifications. Chief among these were that it should be a pleasant area exuding 'Englishness', and that it would be within reasonable road and rail reach of London's main airports, so a potential owner could easily slip in a visit during a trip on other business.

There is hardly a town in the whole country which would not fall over itself to welcome a company like Rolls-Royce for the prestige, let alone for the jobs, it would bring. There was, therefore, considerable interest from local councils, many of them in the West Midlands. It is the heartland of the British motor industry but is also studded with some attractive locales, such

as Stratford-upon-Avon. Oxford was a 'possible' too. Each council proposal was carefully examined but, in the end, it was the proposed agreement with a private estate that stood head and shoulders above all else, and that was from Goodwood.

In 1993, Goodwood had launched the Festival of Speed. An event like no other, it was a sheer celebration of speed featuring everything from bicycles to supersonic jets. At its core was a hill climb course, which competitors were encouraged to tackle for fun and outright speed honours, but the main objective for the Festival was as a massive social event. BMW was involved from the outset through its rich history of motor sport. Such is the Festival's reputation today that, in 2003, it attracted more spectators than the British Grand Prix. It was this connection which prompted BMW, in November 1999, to approach Goodwood.

Some commentators expressed surprise, because the area around Chichester has no tradition of heavy industry, let alone car-building. But Rolls-Royce was also looking for a local workforce skilled in special crafts, and all along the south coast of England are small yards making handbuilt boats. Furthermore, being an affluent part of the country, West Sussex is home to many companies specialising in cabinetmaking and antique furniture restoration; within a 10-mile radius of Chichester it is easier to buy antique furniture than new tables and chairs.

People inside Rolls-Royce refer to the 'Goodwood Experience' being the decisive factor in making the area the company's final choice for a new location. It is difficult to see how anywhere else could match it. It has a unique combination of sport, heritage and elegance, centred on one of the most beautiful country houses and estates in Britain.

Rolls-Royce Motor Cars would be close to Goodwood Motor Circuit. How close? The width of Madgwick Lane, which gives its name to the fabulous double-apex right-hand bend after the start/finish straight, often cited among the top 10 corners for excitement in motor racing history. Still, the distance between Goodwood's main gate and Rolls-Royce's main gate is several hundred yards, so the plant is not quite attached to the pits!

The Goodwood Motor Circuit was active between 1948 and 1966 and hosted Formula One races, the Tourist Trophy and the Goodwood Nine-Hours. It was closed to racing in the mid-1960s because of the safety concerns associated with increased cornering speeds. The site of the circuit is roughly triangular and, since there are public roads on two of the sides, it could not be extended. The choice was between wider run-off areas, or spectator space; both could not be accommodated.

Although the circuit closed for racing, it was used for minor motor sport events and was for a time a testing venue favoured by the motor racing industry. Eventually the Revival Meeting relaunched the great circuit in 1998. Goodwood had become the circuit of choice for most Formula 1 teams because of its variety of corners, and it also offered privacy, being tucked away off the more beaten tracks. In 1973, however, a Surtees-Cosworth Formula 1 car drowned out lessons in the nearby village school, and not unreasonably, the school complained. Goodwood's owner Frederick, the ninth Duke of Richmond & Gordon ordered noise restrictions. Formula 1, 2 and 3 teams continued to practice at Goodwood, but silencers were fitted.

The arrangement worked perfectly well but, in the early 1980s, the noise from the valve gear of high-revving engines could no longer be dampened by silencers alone, and the teams were forced to abandon the circuit. The Goodwood Motor Circuit is still open for testing most days of the year, though, noise is strictly monitored: a computer system alerts marshals to any infringement and also relays information to the local authority.

The council payback for the restrictions was a one-off exception for the annual Goodwood Revival Meeting. This is a magnet for genuine historic racing enthusiasts and, indeed, is now the biggest historic race meeting in Britain. Moreover, it always has a romantic theme, recalling the golden motor sport era of the 1950s and 1960s. With most visitors in period dress (men must wear jackets and ties in the paddock – and mobile phones are banned), it resembles a giant filmset.

The circuit is the boundary of a grass airfield; it was originally laid as an airstrip perimeter road because, during the Second World War from 1940 to 1945, the field was RAF Westhampnett, an auxiliary airfield to the main Fighter Command base at nearby Tangmere.

Rolls-Royce Motor Cars' new manufacturing plant would be directly under the flight path for the old airfield, and every fighter plane which took off from RAF Westhampnett had been powered by a Rolls-Royce engine. In all, 23 squadrons were based there, often only

Top: the pageantry and spectacle of a day at the Goodwood races (photo by Mike Caldwell).

Right: horse racing in its full glory (photo by T Jones).

Below: a touch of class in the members' enclosure (photo by Mike Caldwell).

briefly, and all but the very first used Spitfires. Indeed, Madgwick Lane, which takes the visitor to Rolls-Royce, was closed during the Second World War because of this flight path.

That is a little detail of history. More important is the fact Rolls-Royce clients can arrive in a light plane or helicopter. In line with initial specifications, Heathrow and Gatwick airports are within a two-hour drive, and it is also a two-hour drive to the centre of London. So a potential owner flying to London on a business trip might easily incorporate a visit to Goodwood.

The Goodwood Estate is also internationally famous for its horse-racing track, which has been operating for more than 200 years. It is, by common consent, one of the most beautiful racetracks there is. Within two miles of the Rolls-Royce site there is a four-star hotel, two golf courses, a magnificent stately home (Goodwood House), a Sculpture Park, a 900-year old cathedral often described as the 'most English of cathedrals', and two theatres. The Chichester Festival Theatre and its sister, the Minerva, frequently feature international stars, and productions which originate there and often transfer to London's West End. Close by too, is Cowdray Park, a centre for polo, and the Solent estuary is about seven miles away for yachting fanatics. The Isle of Wight, which can be seen from the racetrack, hosts one of yachting's major events, Cowes Week, and also boasts the finest shark fishing in Europe.

These points have nothing to do with the building of cars. But they have everything to do with the wider experience of becoming a Rolls-Royce owner. A trip to the facility can be linked with many other pursuits, and Phantoms are often bought by people who sail yachts, fly planes, play golf, own horses or polo ponies, and enjoy evenings at the theatre.

Furthermore, the Rolls-Royce facility lies at the foot of the South Downs, an area officially designated as one of Outstanding Natural Beauty. It is a range of hills (only the English could call a hill a 'Down') at the base of which is a flat coastal plain. Since no geographical feature in England is extreme, the coastal plain is, at most, eight miles wide and it is there that Rolls-Royce Motor Cars is now nestled.

The geography is important to understanding the construction of the plant. To put it bluntly, if you are enjoying a walk along the South Downs, you do not want to look down and see a car factory, even if it is on the coastal plain just beyond the 'Area of

Above left: the magnificent Goodwood House ballroom laid out for dinner.

Above right: Goodwood House, the perfect English stately home (photo by Mike Caldwell).

Outstanding Natural Beauty' zone. The environment had to be respected. However, the site offered an unusual advantage: it had permission for the extraction of gravel. This meant that enough gravel could be extracted to create a site in which the Rolls-Royce facility could be built and then sympathetically landscaped. The extraction of gravel would also turn the site from 'greenfield' to 'brownfield', which has a beneficial effect on planning permission.

Construction is detailed in following chapters. But there were two other local links to Rolls-Royce, one known to everyone with an interest in the marque's 100-year old history, and one that few behind the project knew. The first is that Sir Henry Royce spent many of his later years about 10 miles down the road at West Wittering, which overlooks the English Channel. Rolls-Royce enthusiasts have frequently used West Wittering as a focal point for club rallies.

What is not as widely known is that, when he was aged 12, Lord March's grandfather, who was then Freddie Gordon-Lennox, cycled with his elder brother Coldham to visit Sir Henry. Both boys were fascinated by engineering. Charles, Lord Settrington, wanted to be an apprentice at Rolls-Royce because he wanted to learn engineering and was prepared to roll up his sleeves and start from the ground up. However, he was killed in the First World War and his younger brother Freddie took on his title of Lord Settrington. As his forbears had before him, eventually Freddie became first the Earl of March and then the Duke of Richmond & Gordon.

He had been at Oxford University studying agriculture. However, since Freddie spent most of his time riding his motorcycles and tinkering with cars, he was told he was unlikely to graduate so, as plain 'Freddie Settrington', he changed direction and underwent training as a mechanic at the service depot of Bentley Motors.

Bentley's service depot dealt with cars which had been well used and, with so many horses around in the 1920s, the underside of any car was not a pristine environment. Although heir to the dukedom

After many weeks of delicate negotiations, the commitment to build the Rolls-Royce manufacturing plant and head office on Goodwood soil is finally agreed by Lord March (left) and Karl-Heinz Kalbfell (right).

of Richmond & Gordon, Freddie was prepared to lie on his back on a concrete floor and service cars.

His parents doubted he would persevere but he proved them wrong. and when they called him to Scotland for the fishing and shooting season, he pointed out that, as a mechanic at Bentley, he received two weeks' holiday a year and he preferred to use his time as he wished. He would not take more than his two weeks because that would let down his workmates. Despite this rift with his parents, Freddie worked his way up to becoming a mechanic on the Bentley racing team, which he earned on merit. He regarded this as a highlight of his life.

Freddie also designed the 'Brakevan', the world's first multi-purpose vehicle as we know it today in the form of the people-carrier, and he took out patents to prove it. Most Brakevans were built on Ford chassis, but at least one was built on a Rolls-Royce platform, and it was the one that appeared in Brakevan advertisements. These were accompanied by a fulsome testimonial from 'a Sussex driver'. Nobody has ever discovered who the 'Sussex driver' was, but Freddie lived in Sussex! He qualified as a pilot, even though he was prone to air-sickness, and he co-founded the Hordern-Richmond Aircraft Company which developed an experimental

Above left: Lord March has revived the spirit of motor sport at Goodwood that was fostered by his grandfather (photo by Mike Caldwell).

Above right: Lord March tries a historic Jaguar D type for size.

Below right: the Festival of Speed has become an international event in just a decade (photo by Mike Caldwell).

commuter light plane called the 'Autoplane'. Hordern-Richmond (it was typical of Freddie that he gave his boyhood friend, Edmund Hordern, top billing) also manufactured a wood laminate used for variable-pitch aircraft propellers.

When the Second World War broke out, Freddie served in the RAF and Hordern-Richmond was sold to the 'Rotol' consortium, which was Bristol Engines and Rolls-Royce. The laminate is, apparently, still being made today.

Through Freddie Richmond, Goodwood became synonymous not only with horse racing but also motor racing. An earlier Lord March had organised horse races for his regiment there in 1800. Its success prompted him to build a permanent track, which required him to cut a slice from the top of the South Downs.

This story helps to put the protracted negotiation of locating Project Rolls-Royce at Goodwood into perspective. There was a time when the local lord could slice a chunk from the South Downs to create a racetrack simply if he chose to. Nobody could stop him, and he created something extraordinary. It is another thread in the story.

Right: modern Formula 1 machinery is still tested on the Goodwood Circuit and the test hill, but the noise has to be kept down (photo by John Colley).

Below left: fast-paced action at the Goodwood Revival sees Lister-Jaguars and Jaguar D types jostling for position (photo by Paul Hulbert).

Below right: exciting grid for the TT race at the Goodwood Revival Meeting (photo by Mike Caldwell)

The main meeting of the year at the horse racetrack, always at the end of July, is known throughout the world as 'Glorious Goodwood'. King Edward VII once described it as "A garden party with a race meeting attached." Freddie Richmond was able to transfer the track's ambience to the Goodwood Motor Circuit, which had an atmosphere like no other: spectators were made to feel like guests. That great driver of the 1950s, Roy Salvadori, once said: "Give me Goodwood on a summer's day, and you can keep the rest of the world."

Goodwood became the inheritor of the tradition of Brooklands, the world's first permanent motor racing venue. Freddie Richmond had been president of the Brooklands Automobile Racing Club, but Brooklands closed for racing in 1939.

In effect, Goodwood inherited the tradition of the whole of British motor racing. Half-a-century later, it also welcomed that most august of British car marques: Rolls-Royce.

"A garden party with a race meeting attached" – KING EDWARD VII

18 CREATING A NEW HOME FOR ROLLS-ROYCE MOTOR CARS

What we set out to create was a modern, light and airy working environment … where everyone who worked or visited felt part of a continuum dedicated to making something very special

– SIR NICHOLAS GRIMSHAW

Opposite: it was the wishes of the planning authority, and the challenge to Sir Nicholas Grimshaw, that the manufacturing plant and head office would enhance, not conflict with, England's green and pleasant land.

Chichester was founded by the Romans more than 1900 years ago and the centre of the city is still in the Roman pattern. There is a city wall which is roughly circular, and it is bisected by a simple cross of streets, logically entitled North, South, East and West. Almost anyone can walk the length of any of the streets in three or four minutes. Chichester is not a large city.

Chichester is, however, the county town of West Sussex, where the administrative offices and county law courts are located. A great many people come to work here each day from outlying villages.

Put these two facets together, and it is a formula for gridlock. And traffic became an essential element in the negotiations to locate Rolls-Royce on the outskirts of Chichester. Stipulations laid down by local planning authorities meant the company would be obliged to sponsor a car-sharing scheme for employees, while lorries bringing the main components, and departing with completed cars, would have to move at pre-agreed times.

The Goodwood Estate had already gone through a complicated planning application in order to stage historic motor racing at the Goodwood Circuit. Local people had broadly split into two camps: the native 'Cicestrians' (a Cicestrian, by the way, pronounces the name of the city as 'Chidester', with a 'd'); and the incomers, many of whom have retired to what they see only as a quiet cathedral city.

People who had grown up in Chichester welcomed Rolls-Royce to Goodwood, as they had broadly supported the return of motor racing to the circuit there, despite the fact that, in places, the track is only a few hundred yards away from the city's fringes. More recent residents tended to bring up more objections, particularly in relation to noise. One letter to a local newspaper even complained about the sound of a Spitfire aeroplane based at Goodwood, despite the airfield there having been in continuous use since 1940. How could anyone complain about the sound of a Rolls-Royce Merlin engine? It is, surely, the mechanical equivalent of Elgar. Another letter expressed concern at the noise of Rolls-Royces being tested on the circuit, despite the fact the cars have always been among the world's quietest!

But the planning permission Rolls-Royce Motor Cars sought was specific. None of the main components for its cars were to be made at Goodwood: it was to be a facility with the manufacturing element centred around traditional coachwork crafts. The planning application had to go through all its various processes but it proved a much easier task than gaining permission for the revived circuit. The Goodwood Revival Meeting had been dependent on the circuit gaining planning permission: Goodwood's opening bid was for 14 days of racing a year and was settled at five; so far, there have

The manufacturing plant and head office site as purchased. The gravel pit can be seen in the centre of the picture.

only ever been three days of racing a year. Even then, there were objections that had bordered on the ferocious.

What objectors to building a factory on arable land had not picked up on, was that the Goodwood Estate's primary business is farming and forestry. It has a long history of care for one of the most beautiful areas of England. The horse-racing track, for example, has had permanent extensions made to it in the form of new grandstands, and Goodwood has always sought the best architecture for such projects and expected that they would never detract from the beauty of Goodwood House and its surroundings. Thus, Goodwood was acutely conscious that it did not wish to present an eyesore to the many people who use the South Downs for rambling, riding, or cycling.

Happily, however, there was no concerted campaign against Rolls-Royce. The local council did not take much persuasion that the prestige of Rolls-Royce, together with the creation of 350 jobs, was what mattered most. As a side issue, the land already had permission for gravel extraction and, once excavated, may well have become simply a landfill site for waste. A formal application for planning permission for the site was lodged in November 2000 and, after all the extensive consultation, local planning permission was granted in May 2001 and full permission, including Governmental approval, was announced in July of that year. The British Government warmly welcomed such a major investment in the south of England as BMW announced it would spend £65m on building a new home for Rolls-Royce at Goodwood.

Local consultation had indicated there would be a general level of support for the project if BMW approached environmental issues with sympathy. But any design for a manufacturing plant and head office had to not only meet the levels of excellence demanded by Rolls-Royce, but also welcome and cater to many thousands of anticipated visitors.

Several architects tendered for the prestigious work but the final selection of Nicholas Grimshaw & Partners was highly apposite. Grimshaw had previously created the internationally-acclaimed Eden Project in Cornwall, which had turned an enormous hole in the ground, from which china clay had once been extracted, into an incredible botanical wonderland by using a series of glazed domes to roof in this man-made canyon. It had been a vast undertaking, with many critics, but it has been a fabulous success in every way possible.

Left: early days on the building site. Note artist's impression of completed site on the builder's signboard.

Right: a view across the site to the spires of Goodwood racecourse.

Likewise, Grimshaw's design suggested that the gravel should be excavated and the new buildings constructed partially below ground level, with the shape of the building planned to follow the natural contours of the landscape.

The overall layout of the plant was straightforward. Basically, any car made at a rate of more than one a week should, logically be assembled in a straight line. To that long main block, two side wings for offices and showroom were added at right angles, with every part of the facility interlinked, and a courtyard was cradled on three sides by the building. An imposing main entrance would lead directly on to the courtyard. A 'wall of light', with floor-to-ceiling glazing, would open up the assembly process to view from the courtyard and add to the light and space within the production area.

Car parks, lorry parks and storage units were placed at the back. Effectively, there would be two aspects to the plant: a beautiful modern building to greet the visitor at the front, and a fully-functioning industrial facility to the rear. But the facility also had to blend with the landscape – to be visually attractive while being wholly functional. The first consideration was the view from the Sussex Downs, and the whole site would be landscaped to disguise the buildings. This was enhanced by the planting of shrubs and deciduous trees, an amazing 400,000 in all. The official postal address is the tiny village of Westhampnett and it is possible to drive through the village with the buildings mere yards away and not see it. Sir Nicholas Grimshaw stated his brief.

"The intention was to create a finely crafted contemporary building that works in harmony with its natural setting," he said. "In this way, the new manufacturing plant and head offices reflect the ethos behind the Rolls-Royce name, where technology and tradition are brought together with remarkable effect."

Grimshaw, chairman of the architectural practice, was determined the new manufacturing plant and head office would fully reflect the spirit of Rolls-Royce.

"What we set out to create was a modern, light and airy working environment where specialised technologies linked harmoniously with traditional craft skills, and where everyone who worked or visited felt part of a continuum dedicated to making something very special, in a very special place.

"We've used natural materials wherever possible and integrated the whole site into the rural landscape to provide an innovative working environment."

An artistic impression of
the completed manufacturing
plant and head office by
Sir Nicholas Grimshaw.

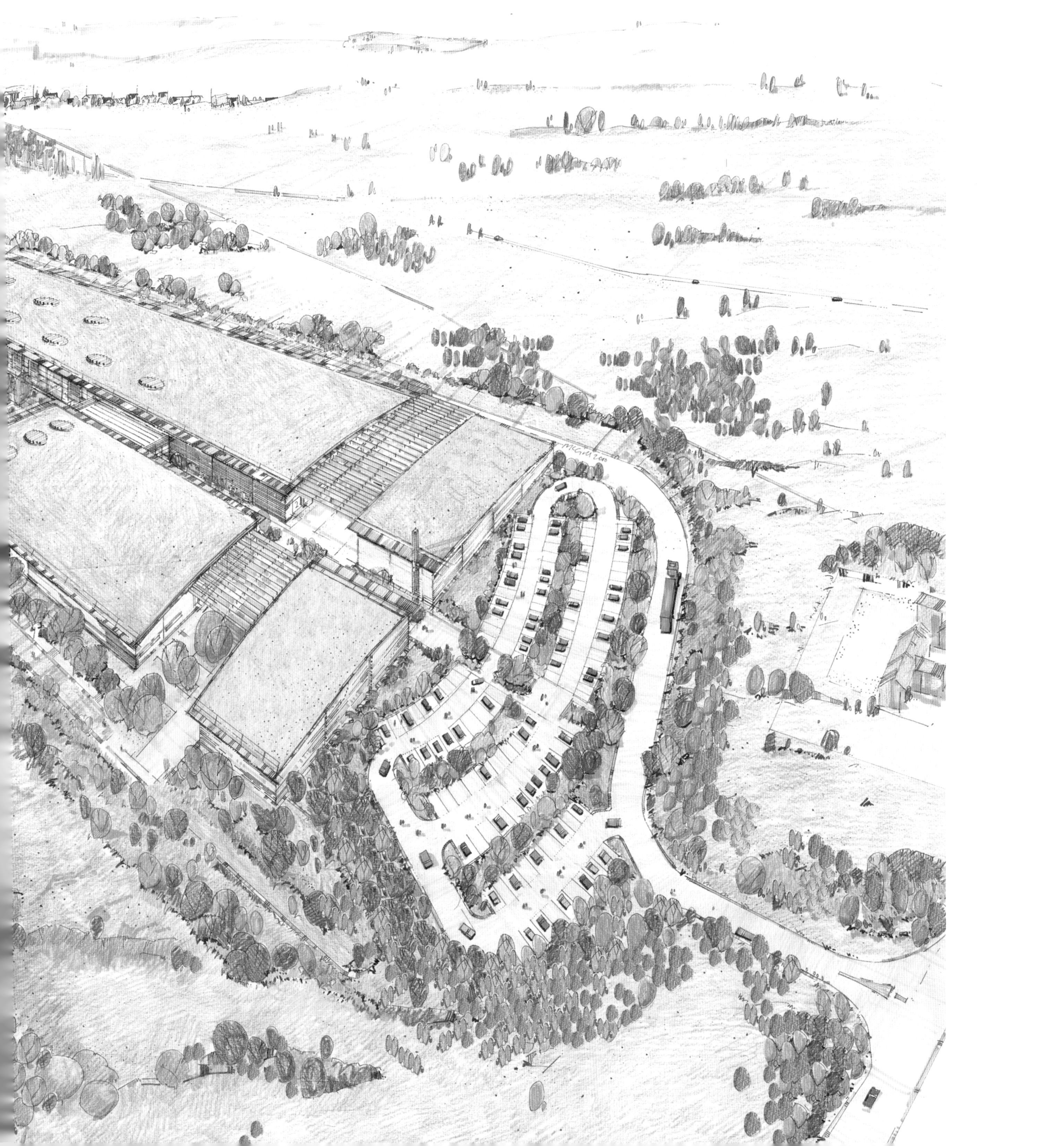

Above: a view of things to come – in early Summer 2001, the future home of Rolls-Royce Motor Cars was still a corn field. Project Director Karl-Heinz Kalbfell surveys the work ahead (photo by Dirk Eisermann).

Right: hundreds of years of Sussex farmland about to take on a new lease of life as the site of the county's premier manufacturing plant.

Above: the visitor meeting area on the first floor of the head office building. Note the 'signature' rotunda skylight.

Above right: the impressive man-made lake at the Westhampnett site.

The whole focus of the site was around its central courtyard, approached by a causeway over a lake and surrounded by extensive landscaping. The roof of the low-rise main building was to be planted with sedum, intended to change colour with the seasons, which would create one of Europe's largest 'living roofs'. This planting was designed to bring economic benefits in addition to providing camouflage for the manufacturing plant and head office buildings when viewed from the South Downs, the 'biomass' on top of the building adding excellent insulation to the roof, so cutting down on excessive heat losses.

The man-made lake is a feature of the overall design. It is there not solely for aesthetic reasons, however. While it is a bonus that Rolls-Royce workers would be able to glance out of the building and see the calming vista of water, the lake was designed to function as a heat-exchanger for the air-conditioning system, using far less electricity than a conventional system, and also assisting with drainage for the whole site.

Grimshaw's building is the most original, environmentally-aware and energy-efficient plant and headquarters anywhere in the motor industry, reflecting the theme of uncompromising excellence. It was a central tenet of the whole project right from the start.

19 A GROUND-BREAKING BUILDING COMES TO LIFE

Our role is to produce the finest car, to the most exacting standards in the world motor industry – TONY GOTT

Opposite: night-time lighting shows the buildings' cedar cladding extremely well.

The entire Project Rolls-Royce team's task was to make sure that the first Phantom was handed over on 1 January 2003.

But, first, the manufacturing team had to oversee the design, development and structure of the site at Goodwood. Dieter Udelhoven, head of manufacturing at Rolls-Royce, also had to design and install the assembly line and all its services, the office facilities to support the manufacturing plant and a myriad other departments – from the staff restaurant to the first aid station. As if that was not enough, he had to create the worldwide network of component suppliers.

Udelhoven recalls: "The fact we were starting with a greenfield site gave us the chance to make the location ideal for Rolls-Royce to produce customised cars for each owner. We had to ask ourselves what requirements we needed, for example, to send different vehicles down the same production line. Had we planned enough flexibility on the site? My view was that we should have enough space to redesign the manufacturing flow for whatever future requirements may be."

Staffing of the manufacturing plant was another task for the Project Rolls-Royce management to oversee, and careful choices were made for each individual job.

"This was a very difficult and interesting task, because our target from the beginning was to create a 'mixed' team with a lot of specialists and craftsmen," says Udelhoven. In the event, as well as staff from the two home nations, the UK and Germany, 10 additional nationalities are represented, including South Africans, Brazilians and other Europeans. Over 6,000 applications were received for the anticipated few hundred jobs available.

Recruits were scrupulously trained, both in Germany and the UK. Local education facilities were used in Chichester to hone some of the specialist craft skills, while the more technical engineering aspects were learned at BMW Group facilities in Germany.

By May 2001, the manufacturing team moved to Goodwood to witness the start of building excavations and the massive movements of gravel which were completed in time for building construction to begin in August. There were just 17 months to go until New Year's Day, 2003!

Time was so pressing that work on the production buildings had to start immediately, and continue throughout the winter months; Udelhoven had installed lines many times before, but never on a half-finished building site! BMW and Rolls-Royce engineers were holding meetings in freezing rooms, often with plastic sheeting instead of windows.

They then pulled on their wellington boots and descended on to the muddy area that would be the shopfloor, although at this time without walls, and a

Above left and right: the steelwork is erected at the end of 2002.

Opposite top left and right: building work at Goodwood proceeds on schedule, with meetings often held in half-built rooms.

Opposite below left: the cedar cladding reflects the winter sunlight.

Opposite below right: preparations were made to install the manufacturing equipment while the building work was still in progress.

main roof that had not been fixed in place due to bad weather conditions.

During November 2001, the erection of the steelwork was started. There must surely have been some mutterings about the speed of the progress, but Karl-Heinz Kalbfell inspired them all to greater efforts and the planned pace was resumed. Unbelievably, bearing in mind that the production line machinery only started to be installed in March 2002, the first prototype Phantom to be made on the line at Goodwood appeared absolutely on time during May, with the first pre-production car just one month later. By November 2002, 35 more cars had been completed, which were subsequently used for shows, photography and exhibitions.

The buildings cover 33,000 square metres of the 170,000 square metres of the site (in more traditional parlance, that is eight acres out of the total 42 acres; one of the original Rolls-Royce criteria was for a site of between 30 and 50 acres), and the remaining area was devoted almost entirely to landscaping. By spring 2003, the massive tree and shrub planting was also completed. It will take a few years but, when these plants mature, they will encase the manufacturing plant and head office complex in a mass of green that will resemble nothing so much as lush parkland, blending in effortlessly with the surrounding Goodwood area.

Much of the manufacturing plant and head office which is not glazed is clad with Canadian cedar, chosen for the way it will season with the weather. This is true even of the storage warehouses at the rear. The use of Canadian cedar cladding extends to the slatted louvres of the 'blinds' of the building. Lighting costs are reduced thanks to the huge glass walls which run the full length of the assembly area, but the computer controlled louvre-blind system automatically controls the amount of light entering the buildings depending on the strength and angle of the sun. A series of eight-metre diameter glass roof lights, which are supported on metal columns with extending spars like tree branches, add further to the natural light and are a design theme which runs throughout the buildings.

These and other energy-saving measures result in attractively lower operating expenses at both the head office and the manufacturing plant building.

True to the Grimshaw blueprint, the 'surface treatment centre', or paintshop, occupies 6,600 square metres, including the two fully-automated spray booths and curing oven; the wood shop beside the assembly line is 1,600 square metres; and the leather shop 2,400 square metres, including sewing areas. The assembly line itself is by far the largest area, occupying 12,300 square metres to accommodate the 19 work stations where 2,000 individual assembly tasks are carried out. Each Phantom will spend some ninety minutes at each station as it is skilfully brought to life.

Each complete car will then undergo extensive inspection and proving in a series of test compartments

nationwide
023 8060 2227
nationwide

Above left and right: the site comes together, with the muddy environs prior to the start of the landscaping process.

at the end of the assembly process in a 3,400 square metre test and validation area. As part of its quality commitment, the Goodwood manufacturing facility recently gained British quality management system accreditation to the ISO9000 standard.

When the Goodwood manufacturing plant and head office officially opened on May 10 2003, Rolls-Royce chairman Tony Gott declared: "By starting afresh, Rolls-Royce has managed to create a modern fusion of the best craftsmanship, the best technology and the best infrastructure without being bogged down by old practices." The new Rolls-Royce manufacturing plant and head office combine Rolls-Royce's inherent tradition of highly skilled craftsmanship with the most sophisticated and modern manufacturing techniques in the world. "Our role is to produce the finest car, to the most exacting standards in the world motor industry. To that end we have designed the plant with the utmost care and have recruited the best people to carry on proudly the Rolls-Royce tradition of craftsmanship."

Perhaps it was the *International Herald Tribune* newspaper that best summed up the dawning era for Rolls-Royce in September 2002: 'Next 1 January, Rolls-Royce will formally take up residence in surroundings more appropriate to its status,' it reported. 'Its new factory is on the estate of the Earl of March at Goodwood, about 200 miles south [of Crewe], in an area of honey-coloured stone houses and gently rolling Downs.'

Truly, the Phantom had arrived at Goodwood.

Above left and right: acres of glass being put into place on the almost-finished manufacturing plant.

Middle left: the main administration block under construction.

Middle right: a view of the 'the bridge' staff restaurant which links the administration building to the manufacturing plant.

Below: Tony Gott's office at the right-hand corner of the head office building.

The production line at night. The assembly line staff have gone home and the cars await further attention upon their return.

The finished manufacturing plant and head office is at its most impressive at night, with the assembly process lit up behind large glass walls.

20 A WALK THROUGH THE MANUFACTURING PLANT

H Royce. Mechanic – HOW SIR HENRY ROYCE SIGNED HIMSELF, TO HIS DYING DAY

Opposite: dramatic views of the immaculate production line, more like a laboratory than a car plant, are offered from overhead walkways.

A visit to Rolls-Royce Motor Cars is unlike a visit to any other car factory. There is no security barrier, nor a guard in a quasi-military uniform at the customer entrance. The attitude appears to be: "If people want to take a look, then why not?" No doubt, there are stringent security operations in place (there certainly are in the industrial part at the rear, and these are overt), but the guest sees only elegant wrought iron gates upon arrival.

When a visitor is shown around the site, the light and space are immediately evident. There appears to be no entrance, only a massive wall of glass, but then panels slide back to allow admission. Then there is the quietness: if the visitor were taken in blind-folded and asked to guess what was happening here, he would probably say it was a laboratory developing medicines.

The reception area is larger than many car showrooms and, as might be expected, there are also cars on display here. Rolls-Royce is delighted when owners choose to collect their new cars directly from the manufacturing plant. This opportunity is automatically offered although, in practice, most Phantom customers – even if they have been to Goodwood many times – tend to prefer to have their cars delivered.

The widespread use of glass is one reason why security measures are so unobtrusive: everything is open to view. This includes any meeting taking place in the special, open-plan area set aside for discussions that anyone working on the assembly line can easily see. In a similar vein, there is only one restaurant where every employee eats – and very good it is too.

A traditional Rolls-Royce service is to offer customers the opportunity to visit at any stage during the construction of their cars and discuss the progress being made. A remarkable experience for such a visitor is that the assembly line seems relaxed and quiet. When one work station has completed its task on a Phantom, the car is pushed serenely to the next. One of the very few automated stages is at the point where the body/spaceframe is lifted to accept the powertrain. Only then are powered hoists employed.

The Sir Henry Royce Institute, the plant's newly-established, in-house training section, is located immediately adjacent to the assembly line, so any manufacturing issue can be demonstrated or examined quickly at close quarters. Sir Henry is a constant presence at the facility: the visitor meets his photograph as he or she enters the reception area, and his exacting standards are obvious everywhere else.

With the main assembly proceeding at an apparently unhurried pace, small specialist units alongside produce the bespoke wooden and leather trim. It is easy to find oneself engaged in a conversation by one of the craftsmen – and he or she will usually open

Opposite: body and drivetrain now together, work begins on interior connections. The Spirit of Ecstasy mascot, already fitted, is in its security position.

Above: a door capping is trimmed and sanded down, prior to the high gloss finish being applied.

Right: hard work, a deft touch and a skilled eye cannot be replaced by a machine for this job – the veneer for a door fillet is rubbed down before lacquering.

A door, supported on its transport frame, receives window glass and rubber seal.

Early days – the first pre-production car to be completed at Goodwood stars with a full supporting cast of its makers.

the dialogue. On an individual trip, the visitor is often pounced on by a worker eager to talk about his passion. It might be one of the master woodworkers, as on a visit by the author, and his enthusiasm was infectious. It is always a pleasure to meet someone who is both an expert and an enthusiast.

This man was previously a restorer of antique furniture and was bringing his understanding of wood to the Phantom. The vividness of the grain in oak is different to the grain in ash, he explained; the challenge for him is to supply woodwork that will give pleasure to the owner for as long as he keeps the car.

There are some small but significant items to notice upon walking around the assembly line. For instance, a Phantom will normally have two sheets of specifications attached to its front wings; a 'bespoke' Phantom will have several sheets. Close-scrutiny inspection carries on all the time, but it is discreet. One may see a bodyshell which appears perfect to the layman's eye. It has, after all, been fabricated on the most accurate and up-to-date of machinery. But it may be covered in dozens of white marks each of which represents a blemish, detected by an expert and fastidiously earmarked for attention.

When the last inspection has been completed, a Phantom is placed on four hydraulic jacks which can be programmed to simulate any road in the world. If there are squeaks or rattles, the car is returned to the production line. The next test rig is a rolling road, which can assess all the performance characteristics of the car and, as importantly, all the electronic systems. Then follows the 'monsoon test', a name coined by Rolls-Royce staff, where a Phantom is subjected to spraying by 73 high pressure water jets. This test is designed to discover even a pinprick leak.

Once it has passed through all those tests, it is driven around the lanes near Goodwood. Consider this: someone is actually paid to drive Rolls-Royce Phantoms on the lanes of Sussex all day. How does one come by a job like that?

TECHNICAL SPECIFICATIONS

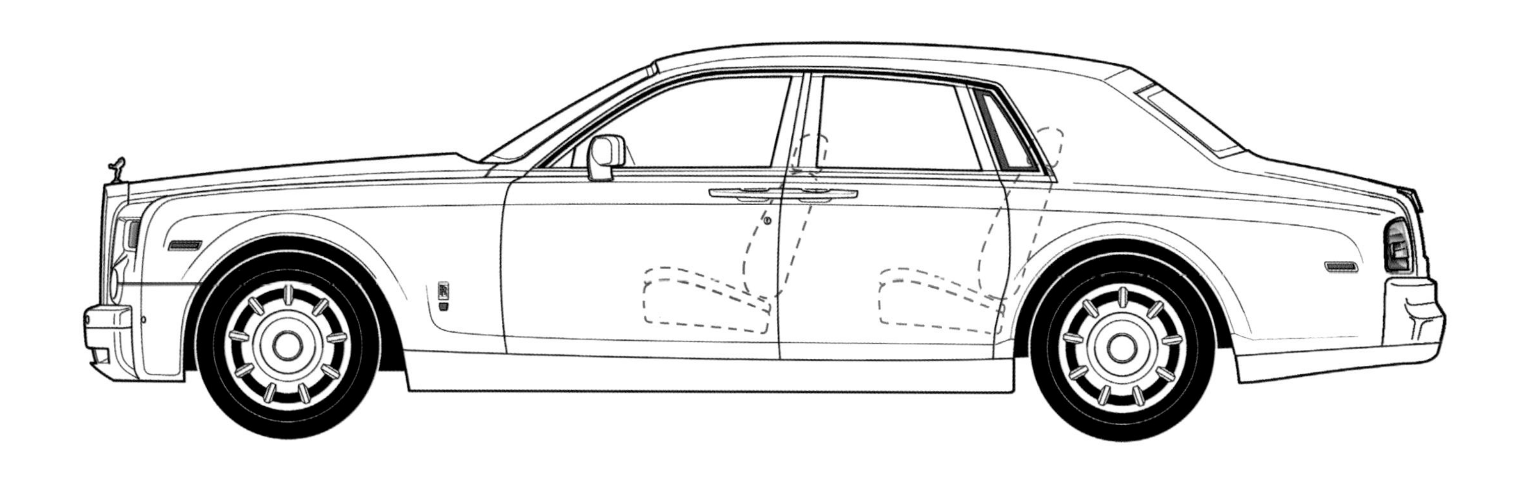

No. of doors/seats	4 / 5
Vehicle length	5834 mm / 229.7 ins
Vehicle width	1990 mm / 78.3 ins
Vehicle height, unladen	1632 mm / 64.3 ins
Wheelbase	3570 mm / 140.6 ins
Turning circle	13.8 m / 45.3 ft
Track, front	1685 mm / 66.3 ins
Track, rear	1670 mm / 65.7 ins
Width at shoulder height, front	1509 mm / 59.4 ins
Width at shoulder height, rear	1431 mm / 56.3 ins
Leg room, front	1028 mm / 40.5 ins
Leg room, rear	947 mm / 37.3 ins
Head room, front	1020 mm / 40.2 ins
Head room, rear	979 mm / 38.5 ins

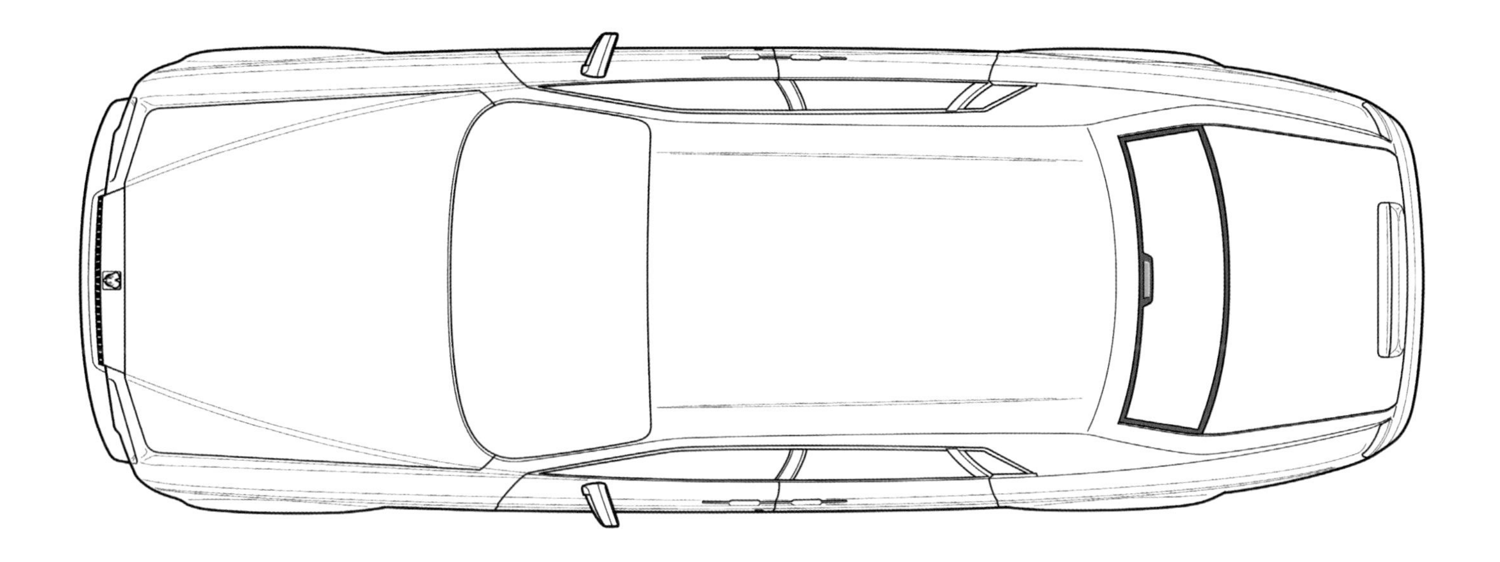

Boot volume	460 ltr / 16.2 cu ft
Fuel tank capacity	100 ltr / 22 imp gal
Unladen weight	2,495 kg / 5,489 lbs
Axle load ratio, rear (unladen)	49.9 %
Gross vehicle weight	3,050 kg / 6,710 lbs
Payload	555 kg / 1,221 lbs
Axle load limit, front	1,425 kg / 3,141 lbs
Axle load limit, rear	1,800 kg / 3,968 lbs
Engine / valves	60°V12 / 48
Fuel management	Direct injection
Displacement	6,749 cc / 411.8 cu in
Stroke	84.6 mm / 3.33 ins
Bore	92.0 mm / 3.62 ins

Power output @ engine speed	453 bhp / 460 PS (DIN) / 338 kW @ 5,350 rpm
Max. torque @ engine speed	531 lb ft / 720 Nm @ 3,500 rpm
Compression ratio	11:1
Transmission type	ZF 6HP32
Gear ratios:	
1st	4.171
2nd	2.340
3rd	1.521
4th	1.143
5th	0.867
6th	0.691
Reverse	3.403
Final drive ratio	3.460
Steering type	Rack and pinion, speed-sensitive variable rate power assistance
Brakes:	
Front / diameter	Disc vent. 374 mm / 14.7 ins
Rear / diameter	Disc vent. 370 mm / 14.6 ins

Drag c_d	0.38
Drag c_d x A	1.071 sq. m / 11.5 sq. ft
Top speed	149 mph / 240 km/h
Acceleration 0-60 mph	5.7 sec
Acceleration 0-100 km/h	5.9 sec
Acceleration 0-1,000 m	25.6 sec
EU test cycle:	
Fuel consumption urban	24.6 ltr/100 km/h / 11.5 mpg
Fuel consumption extra urban	11.0 ltr/100 km/h / 25.7 mpg
Fuel consumption combined	15.9 ltr/100 km/h / 17.8 mpg
CO^2 emissions	385 g/km
Tyre size	PAX 265x790 R540A 111W
Wheel size	PAX 265x540A
Radiator incl. heater / Engine oil	14 ltr / 8.5 ltr
Battery capacity / installed position	90+70Ah / boot
Alternator output rating	2 x 180A / 2520W

POSTSCRIPT

This book has been produced independently of Rolls-Royce Motor Cars Ltd., and so I have been under no obligation to enhance the good, nor to glaze over the not-so-good facts, about the Rolls-Royce Phantom. I was able to approach the project with a completely neutral view, although it was my fervent wish that I would find the marque of Rolls-Royce to be in safe hands.

With no guarantee or control over the contents of this book, save an agreed temporary embargo on information concerning the 100EX experimental car until the presentation of the car at the 2004 Geneva show, both Rolls-Royce Motor Cars and BMW have allowed me complete access to facilities, personnel and records concerning Project Rolls-Royce, for which I thank them unreservedly.

It is generally accepted that the new company had but one chance to make a car that could regain the sobriquet of 'The Best Car in the World'. But how can one judge this? There are surely cars that go around corners faster, accelerate faster, stop more quickly, carry more people, use less fuel or can be parked in smaller spaces. There are cheaper cars and there are more expensive cars. There are cars with more electronic wizardry and some that can be driven on rougher terrain. Perhaps a fair judgement of 'best' would be a car that is most able to perform its designed tasks within a chosen market sector.

For me, a car like this one within the super-luxury sector would need to endow its occupants with a feeling of well-being, comfort and authority. It would need to handle without any vices and be a truly satisfying machine to control. It would be a car I would want to wash and polish myself, for the sheer tactile pleasure of ownership.

This car would need to be utterly reliable and go from recommended service to recommended service without niggling faults. No rattles, no squeaks, no leaks.

Most of all, 'The Best Car in the World' would have to be capable of taking myself and my passengers on a long and arduous journey in poor weather conditions and, when we arrived, we would feel less tired and less fraught than had we travelled in any other car.

If the only requirements for designing and building a near-perfect car were enthusiasm and passion, then the members of Project Rolls-Royce would certainly have built 'The Best Car in the World'. In reality, other attributes are clearly needed: engineering design and construction of the highest order, outstanding quality control, and, of course, exterior and interior design without equal.

Did they manage, on this one and only chance, to put the Spirit of Ecstasy back on her pedestal? Yes, they did! As I have written, with an almost embarrassing inability to find fault, problems are very few and far between.

A car can only be fairly judged against its peers, but when enthusiasts of the future look back on the first century of Rolls-Royce production, they will remember four models that stand out from the rest: the early Silver Ghost, the Phantom II Continental, the Phantom III and this one, the Phantom of today. No wonder the choice of name was so easy.

Design	Simon Loxley
Printer	The Lavenham Press Suffolk, England
Printing	Five colour litho on Heidelberg Speedmaster
Page Size	280mm x 280mm
Text paper	170gsm Sovereign Silk
End papers	170gsm Sovereign Silk
Dustjacket	Five colour litho on 170gsm Sovereign Silk
Inks	Fishburn Flashdri
Case binding	Wibalin
Body text	9/13pt Sabon